Promising Practices in Mathematics and Science Education:

A Collection of Promising Educational Programs and Practices from the Laboratory Network Program

LABORATORY
NETWORK PROGRAM

Regional Educational Laboratories

Appalachia Educational Laboratory
Charleston, WV

Far West Laboratory for Educational Research and
Development
San Francisco, CA

Mid-continent Regional Educational Laboratory
Aurora, CO

North Central Regional Educational Laboratory
Oak Brook, IL

Northwest Regional Educational Laboratory
Portland, OR

Pacific Region Educational Laboratory
Honolulu, HI

Regional Laboratory for Educational Improvement of the
Northeast and Islands
Andover, MA

Research for Better Schools
Philadelphia, PA

SouthEastern Regional Vision for Education
Greensboro, NC

Southwest Educational Development Laboratory
Austin, TX

This publication is sponsored wholly or in part by the U.S. Department of Education, Office of Educational Research and Improvement, under contract numbers: RP9 1002001, RP9 1002002, RP9 1002003, RP9 1002004, RP9 1002005, RP9 1002006, RP9 1002007, RP9 1002008, RP9 1002009, and RP9 1002010. The content of this publication does not necessarily reflect the views of the department or any other agency of the U.S. Government.

This publication is available from your Regional Educational Laboratory (see page 155). Copies can also be ordered from the Government Printing Office. Call 202-783-3238 for ordering information.

FOREWORD

"By the year 2000, American students will be first in the world in mathematics and science achievement."

National Educational Goal Four

I am pleased to present this volume of promising practices in mathematics education, developed by the ten regional educational laboratories funded by the U.S. Department of Education's Office of Educational Research and Improvement (OERI). The laboratories' collection of programs emerged from a broad-based search, nomination, and review process reaching many educators throughout the United States.

Mathematics and science teachers and other reviewers from higher education institutions, state and local education agencies, regional educational laboratories, museums, foundations, associations, and other organizations selected the 66 practices presented in this guide from among the hundreds that were nominated for consideration. The criteria that reviewers used in selecting these promising practices are outlined on page vii.

This volume of promising practices in mathematics and science education provides an array of innovative ideas for elementary and secondary teachers. As teachers continue their efforts to increase student achievement in mathematics and science, this guide can serve as a ready reference to model programs and practices that are already being used to improve teaching and learning in these fields.

Along with this book, a companion guide to exemplary mathematics and science programs has been produced by OERI's National Diffusion Network program. That guide provides information on programs that have been validated through the Department of Education's Program Effectiveness Panel process. Together, these resources can help us work toward achieving the National Education Goals for mathematics and science education envisioned for the year 2000.

Sharon P. Robinson
Assistant Secretary
Office of Educational Research and Improvement
U.S. Department of Education

Table of Contents

INTRODUCTION

Since the six national goals for education to be reached by the year 2000 were announced in 1989, public approval (as expressed in the Gallup Poll) has been high. The goal that "American students will be first in the world in mathematics and science achievement" was recently rated very high or high by 79 percent of the population. However, people were very skeptical about the possibility of realizing this goal by the year 2000. Indeed, it will not be easy.

Leaders in science and mathematics education are calling for drastic changes in the way science and mathematics are structured, sequenced, and taught. In order to assist schools in making these changes, the regional educational laboratories became involved in the identification of promising programs and practices in mathematics and science instruction. This volume, *Promising Practices in Mathematics and Science Education*, presents the first-year results. Its objective is to broaden awareness and usage of currently available resources to improve student performance in science and mathematics.

The Laboratory Network Program

During the nearly three decades since their inception, the regional educational laboratories (funded by the Office of Educational Research and Improvement of the U.S. Department of Education) have proven to be valuable resources in their regions. Each laboratory identifies regional needs and develops programs to help meet them.

Working together, the regional educational laboratories have become a national asset, able to mount a coherent response to national research and development (R&D) needs and priorities. In cooperation with partners in the state education agencies, universities, and intermediate service agencies, new programs and other resources have been made available to school districts, schools, and the myriad of other agencies and individuals working in education.

The Laboratory Network Program was established in 1992 in recognition of the growing need for coordinated national responses to America's educational challenges, and the potential of the laboratories to help meet this need. All ten have joined together to formalize, consolidate, and extend their capability to act as a national system. This book is one of the results of the first year of the collaborative effort.

Selecting Promising Practices

The programs and practices described in this publication range from individual classroom activities to system-wide multi-grade efforts. The process for selecting the programs involved four stages. During the first stage, each laboratory solicited nominations from its region using a request specifically designed for this purpose. The second stage involved reviews in each region by panels of mathematics and science educators of the nomination information and other descriptive or evaluative information submitted in each region. The criteria used to evaluate each program included a degree of match with national curriculum standards, evidence of effectiveness, and transferability. The third stage involved a national review by representatives from all laboratories to ensure consistency. During the fourth stage, site visits were conducted to confirm that the selected programs or practices were actually as described in the nomination and review materials.

This process resulted in the identification of the 66 programs included in this publication — which are currently being used in individual classrooms and districts throughout the nation. A database containing descriptions of these programs and practices has also been created. The database is searchable using ERIC (Educational Resources Information Center) descriptors and is available on the Internet. These products are supported by the Laboratory Network Program and the Regional Eisenhower Mathematics and Science Consortia through funding from the Office of Educational Research and Improvement. They will be expanded each year.

For further information, contact the regional educational laboratory or Eisenhower Mathematics and Science Consortium in your region (both listed in the appendix).

HOW TO USE THIS BOOK

This book is arranged by topic in the following order: Elementary Mathematics, Elementary Science, Mathematics, Multidisciplinary, Science, and Technology. The practices are in alphabetical order within these designations. If you are searching for specific grade levels, use appendix A on page 147. Programs also appear in overall alphabetical order (see appendix B).

Each program/practice is presented in a two-page layout. The title of each practice appears prominently at the top of the left page, followed by the initiating location and a headline giving a synopsis of the program. Explanations follow of the other descriptors which are presented for each practice; the numbers which are attached to each descriptor below are appropriately placed on the illustrated page opposite.

Explanation of left-hand page layout (refer to page xi)

1. **TOPIC:** This descriptor gives the primary focus of the program. In this case, Algebra is given as the focus.

2. **USER(S):** This category delineates the grade levels where this program has been used successfully and who might be the likely users of this practice. In this example, grade 7-12 teachers, university mathematics educators, and administrators have used this program; however, this does not mean that others cannot use it successfully.

3. **TARGET POPULATION:** This category indicates the particular population for whom this program was designed. For instance, a program may incorporate elements that specifically speak to minority groups or to women in urban settings.

4. **EMPHASIS ON:** Descriptions found in this field indicate the types of instructional materials that are used, teaching strategies that have been incorporated, and assessment tools that are part of the practice. More detailed information on this area may be found in the general description at the bottom of the first page.

5. **GENERAL DESCRIPTION:** This abstract conveys in simple terms what the program is about. It has been generally divided into four subsections:

   - *Innovative Features* - This section addresses what makes this program stand apart from others in this field, i.e., what makes it valuable or different.

   - *Goals* - The major goals are outlined in this section.

   - *Effectiveness* - This section addresses the evaluation of the program. The data portrayed here range from attitude improvements towards mathematics and science to in-depth, long-term assessments supporting success of the program/practice.

   - *Staff Support* - What support services are necessary for effective implementation of this program and what support is available from this agency or other organizations? These issues are dealt with in short form in this section.

title of program

TEACHER TRAINING FOR TECHNOLOGY IN THE MATHEMATICS CLASSROOM

location → University of Central Arkansas
Conway, AR

one-line description

Instructional Technology for Algebra Classrooms

TOPIC: Pre-A Algebra I, Algebra II

 USER(S): 7-12 Educators, University Mathematics Educators, School Administrators

TARGET POPULATION: Urbask, Suburban, Ethnic/Minority, Rural, Female

EMPHASIS ON:

Instructional Materials

- Teaching Lessons/Units
- Technology-Based Materials

Teaching Strategies

- Hands-On Learning
- Student-Centered Learning
- Cooperative/Group Learning
- Technology-Based Strategies

Assessment Tools

- Portfolios
- Technology-Based Tools

5 **GENERAL DESCRIPTION**

Teaching Technology in the Mathematics Classroom assists school districts and teachers in implementing technologically appropriate mathematics instruction. The project is based on the following:

1. the movement led by the National Council of Teachers of Mathematics (NCTM) and the National Research Council to Reform the Teaching of Mathematics,

2. the belief that mathematics should be accessible to all students, and

3. the importance of computer accessibility for all mathematics students.

Innovative Features: This project equips mathematics classrooms with computer hardware, software, and supplemental resources. The project breaks with traditional staff development and emphasizes the development of lessons and units by teachers.

Effectiveness: Forty-five Arkansas algebra teachers from 42 school districts have participated in Teaching Technology in the Mathematics Classroom during the past two years. Ongoing evaluation of the project includes site visits to the schools and follow-up discussion sessions.

Staff Support: A two-week intensive summer institute focuses on assisting teachers in using computer hardware and software, developing computer-based curriculum materials, and using appropriate instructional strategies. Past participants are invited to attend three annual follow-up sessions in which teachers collaborate on lessons, receive additional training, and participate in a support system.

year program was first used → (Year initiated: 1991)

Explanation of right-hand page layouts (refer to page xiii)

6. **GRADE LEVEL:** The graph located in the top right-hand corner of the page shows the grade levels for which the program/practice is best suited.

7. **NCISE STANDARDS MET:** This checklist gives information on standards from the National Center for Improving Science Education that are met through this program. It's important to note that these goals serve as a "placeholder" for standards that are currently being developed by the National Research Council and the 2061 Benchmarks from the American Association for the Advancement of Science.

8. **NCTM STANDARDS MET:** This checklist shows agreement or support of standards published by the National Council of Teachers of Mathematics.

9. **RESOURCES/MATERIALS NEEDED FOR ADOPTION:** This section delineates the types of support necessary for the proper implementation of this program, e.g., special types of classroom equipment and staff support.

10. **FUNDED BY:** Information about past program sponsors is shown here although these sponsors would not necessarily support the establishment of future programs.

11. **CONTACT:** The name of the person who would normally provide information and answer questions about the program/practice appears here. Information may also be acquired from the regional educational laboratory that acted as the source for a particular program.

11a. **SOURCE:** This descriptor indicates the regional educational laboratory which submitted the entry.

12. **SITE(S):** The name of the site or sites where this program has been instituted appears in this segment. This site has successfully implemented the program/ practice and may possibly serve as a demonstration site. (Note: Full addresses are not provided for all sites listed.)

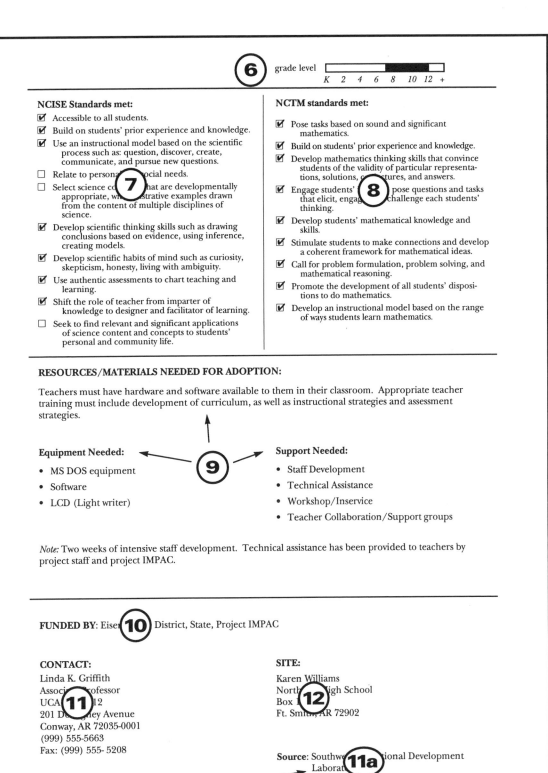

⑥ grade level

K 2 4 6 8 10 12 +

NCISE Standards met:

☑ Accessible to all students.

☑ Build on students' prior experience and knowledge.

☑ Use an instructional model based on the scientific process such as: question, discover, create, communicate, and pursue new questions.

☐ Relate to person⑦ ocial needs.

☐ Select science co⑦ hat are developmentally appropriate, w trative examples drawn from the content of multiple disciplines of science.

☑ Develop scientific thinking skills such as drawing conclusions based on evidence, using inference, creating models.

☑ Develop scientific habits of mind such as curiosity, skepticism, honesty, living with ambiguity.

☑ Use authentic assessments to chart teaching and learning.

☑ Shift the role of teacher from imparter of knowledge to designer and facilitator of learning.

☐ Seek to find relevant and significant applications of science content and concepts to students' personal and community life.

NCTM standards met:

☑ Pose tasks based on sound and significant mathematics.

☑ Build on students' prior experience and knowledge.

☑ Develop mathematics thinking skills that convince students of the validity of particular representations, solutions, c tures, and answers.

☑ Engage students' ⑧ pose questions and tasks that elicit, enga challenge each students' thinking.

☑ Develop students' mathematical knowledge and skills.

☑ Stimulate students to make connections and develop a coherent framework for mathematical ideas.

☑ Call for problem formulation, problem solving, and mathematical reasoning.

☑ Promote the development of all students' dispositions to do mathematics.

☑ Develop an instructional model based on the range of ways students learn mathematics.

RESOURCES/MATERIALS NEEDED FOR ADOPTION:

Teachers must have hardware and software available to them in their classroom. Appropriate teacher training must include development of curriculum, as well as instructional strategies and assessment strategies.

Equipment Needed:

⑨

Support Needed:

• MS DOS equipment

• Software

• LCD (Light writer)

• Staff Development

• Technical Assistance

• Workshop/Inservice

• Teacher Collaboration/Support groups

Note: Two weeks of intensive staff development. Technical assistance has been provided to teachers by project staff and project IMPAC.

FUNDED BY: Eise⑩ District, State, Project IMPAC

CONTACT:
Linda K. Griffith
Associ rofessor
UCA⑪ 12
201 D ey Avenue
Conway, AR 72035-0001
(999) 555-5663
Fax: (999) 555- 5208

SITE:
Karen Williams
North igh School
Box ⑫
Ft. Smith, AR 72902

Source: Southwe ional Development Laborat⑪a

source of entry

MATHEMATICS
ELEMENTARY GRADES

(**Note:** K-12 programs appear in the *Mathematics: Middle Grades - Post Secondary* section of this publication, p.31)

A CONSTRUCTIVIST MATHEMATICS PROGRAM

Hall-Kent Elementary School
Homewood, AL

Elementary Math Program in which Students Learn Underlying Principals of Mathematics for Themselves.

TOPIC: Elementary Math

USER(S): K-5 Educators

TARGET POPULATION: All Students

EMPHASIS ON:

Instructional Materials	Teaching Strategies	Assessment Tools
• N/A	• Hands-On Learning	• N/A
	• Student-Centered Learning	
	• Whole-Language Teaching Approach	
	• Cooperative/Group Learning	
	• Individualized/Self-Paced Learning	

GENERAL DESCRIPTION

This elementary math program is based upon constructivist learning theory in that students discover the underlying principles of mathematics for themselves.

Innovative Features: The program replaces the textbook, workbook, and worksheets with activities involving situations in daily living, as well as games and discussions. Algorithms are not taught, instead children are encouraged to invent their own procedures for the four arithmetical operations. Creativity and critical thinking skills are utilized as students invent many different ways of solving problems. Correct or incorrect answers are not reinforced, instead students are encouraged to exchange viewpoints.

Goals: Students learn to do their own thinking, develop confidence in their ability to figure things out, come to believe that math is logical, and seek truth through exchange of view points.

Effectiveness: Teachers perceive that children in the program understand place value much better than traditionally instructed students.

(Year initiated: 1984)

NCISE Standards met:

☐ Accessible to all students.

☐ Build on students' prior experience and knowledge.

☐ Use an instructional model based on the scientific process such as: question, discover, create, communicate, and pursue new questions.

☐ Relate to personal and social needs.

☐ Select science concepts that are developmentally appropriate, with illustrative examples drawn from the content of multiple disciplines of science.

☐ Develop scientific thinking skills such as drawing conclusions based on evidence, using inference, creating models.

☐ Develop scientific habits of mind such as curiosity, skepticism, honesty, living with ambiguity.

☐ Use authentic assessments to chart teaching and learning.

☐ Shift the role of teacher from imparter of knowledge to designer and facilitator of learning.

☐ Seek relevant and significant applications of science content and concepts to students' personal and community life.

NCTM standards met:

☑ Pose tasks based on sound and significant mathematics.

☑ Build on students' prior experience and knowledge.

☑ Develop mathematics thinking skills that convince students of the validity of particular representations, solutions, conjectures, and answers.

☑ Engage students' intellect; pose questions and tasks that elicit, engage, and challenge each students' thinking.

☑ Develop students' mathematical knowledge and skills.

☑ Stimulate students to make connections and develop a coherent framework for mathematical ideas.

☑ Call for problem formulation, problem solving, and mathematical reasoning.

☑ Promote the development of all students' dispositions to do mathematics.

☑ Develop an instructional model based on the range of ways students learn mathematics.

RESOURCES/MATERIALS NEEDED FOR ADOPTION:

Assorted math games

Equipment Needed:

• N/A

Support Needed:

• Orientation

• Staff Development

Note: Two books and three videotapes authored by C. Kamii and published by Teachers College Press: Young Children Reinvent Arithmetic (1985), Young Children Continue to Reinvent Arithmetic (1989), "Double-Column Addition" (1989), "Multiplication of Two-Digit Numbers" (1990), and "Multidigit Division" (1990).

FUNDED BY: N/A

CONTACT:

SERVE Consortium for Mathematics and Science Education
345 S. Magnolia Dr., Suite D-23
Tallahassee, FL 32301-2950
(904) 922-8533; (800) 854-0476
Fax: (904) 922-8068

SITE(S):

Hall-Kent Elementary School
213 Hall Avenue
Homewood, AL 35209

Source: SouthEastern Regional Vision for Education

ELEMENTARY MATH LEAD TEACHER

School District of Oconee County
Walhalla, SC

A Math Staff Development Program Involving Graduate Credit Courses

TOPIC: Elementary Math

USER(S): K-6 Educators

TARGET POPULATION: Rural, Emotionally Handicapped, At-Risk, Ethnic/Minority, Gifted, Learning Disabled, Elementary School Students

EMPHASIS ON:

Instructional Materials	Teaching Strategies	Assessment Tools
• N/A	• Hands-On Learning	• N/A
	• Student-Centered Learning	
	• Thematic Teaching Approach	
	• Whole Language Approach	
	• Cooperative/Group Learning	
	• Individualized/Self-Paced Learning	
	• Technology-Based Strategies	

GENERAL DESCRIPTION

The **Elementary Math Lead Teacher** Program is a staff development model that improves mathematics instruction in the elementary school.

Innovative Features: Participants must complete 300 hours of coursework, for which they receive graduate credit toward certification as math specialists. Instruction includes MathTools, AIMS (Activities Integrating Math and Science), MCTP (Australian Teacher Training), NCTM membership and training, computer use, cooperative learning, current practice in mathematics education and research, and mathematics content.

Goals: The program goal is to improve mathematics education for all elementary school students, including special needs students.

Effectiveness: Results of a survey administered at the end of the major coursework indicate a significant increase in teacher use of manipulatives and feelings of empowerment in mathematics. In addition, a random sampling of mathematics lessons shows students actively involved in mathematics more than 50% of the time. Teachers lectured, used the overhead projector, and dominated class discussion only 25% of the time.

Staff Support: This approach to staff development needs commitment of the administration and can be implemented through administrative initiatives. Public school and university collaboration is essential. Support of a university-level research mathematician is required.

(Year initiated: 1990)

NCISE Standards met:

☐ Accessible to all students.

☐ Build on students' prior experience and knowledge.

☐ Use an instructional model based on the scientific process such as: question, discover, create, communicate, and pursue new questions.

☐ Relate to personal and social needs.

☐ Select science concepts that are developmentally appropriate, with illustrative examples drawn from the content of multiple disciplines of science.

☐ Develop scientific thinking skills such as drawing conclusions based on evidence, using inference, creating models.

☐ Develop scientific habits of mind such as curiosity, skepticism, honesty, living with ambiguity.

☐ Use authentic assessments to chart teaching and learning.

☐ Shift the role of teacher from imparter of knowledge to designer and facilitator of learning.

Seek relevant and significant applications of science content and concepts to students' personal and community life.

NCTM standards met:

☑ Pose tasks based on sound and significant mathematics.

☑ Build on students' prior experience and knowledge.

☑ Develop mathematics thinking skills that convince students of the validity of particular representations, solutions, conjectures, and answers.

☑ Engage students' intellect; pose questions and tasks that elicit, engage, and challenge each students' thinking.

☑ Develop students' mathematical knowledge and skills.

☑ Stimulate students to make connections and develop a coherent framework for mathematical ideas.

☑ Call for problem formulation, problem solving, and mathematical reasoning.

☑ Promote the development of all students' dispositions to do mathematics.

☑ Develop an instructional model based on the range of ways students learn mathematics.

RESOURCES/MATERIALS NEEDED FOR ADOPTION:

Manipulatives for classroom use.

Teacher Resource Books.

Professional Journals (NCTM).

Australian materials now available from NCTM.

Assorted Instructional Materials.

Interdisciplinary Curriculum Materials.

Equipment Needed:

• Manipulatives

• Math Methods References

• Mathematics References

• A University-Level Research Mathematician

Support Needed:

• Staff Development

• Teacher Collaborations

• Eighteen Hours of Graduate Credit Coursework

FUNDED BY: National Science Foundation, Eisenhower Mathematics and Science Education Program, District, State

CONTACT:

SERVE Consortium for Mathematics
and Science Education
345 S. Magnolia Dr., Suite D-23
Tallahassee, FL 32301-2950
(904) 922-8533; (800) 854-0476
Fax: (904) 922-8068

SITE(S):

School District of Oconee County
P.O. Box 649
Walhalla, SC 29691

Source: SouthEastern Regional Vision for Education

FAMILY MATH & MATEMÁTICA PARA LA FAMILIA

Lawrence Hall of Science, University of California
Berkeley, CA

K-8 Mathematics Program Promotes Family Involvement by Removing Language and Cultural Barriers

TOPIC: Elementary Math

USER(S): K-8 educators, School administrators, Parents, Paraprofessionals, Community Members, Retired People

TARGET POPULATION: All Students

EMPHASIS ON:

Instructional Materials	Teaching Strategies	Assessment Tools
• Teaching Package with Lessons/Units	• Hands-On Learning	• N/A
	• Cooperative/Group Learning	
	• Thematic Teaching Approach	
	• Problem-Based Learning	
	• Family/Student-Centered Learning	

GENERAL DESCRIPTION

Family Math (FM) and **Matemática Para la Familia (MPF)** transform student attitudes towards mathematics and empower parents by giving them a new sense of confidence. They open lines of communication within families and between home and school.

Innovative Features: With FM/MPF, families learn mathematics together in a non-threatening environment. Non-professional educators are able to offer excellent classes in any setting so that people of different ages and levels of experience and knowledge are engaged in meaningful and interesting challenges.

Goals: FM/MPF programs seek to involve families in their children's mathematics education in a positive and effective way. They focus on specific populations (e.g., Spanish speaking) and help the student and adult family member develop greater self-confidence as they perceive themselves able to think mathematically. They raise the awareness that mathematics is important to study.

Effectiveness: In addition to positive formal evaluations, the children like mathematics better, and have increased interest, enthusiasm, and levels of questioning. Parents/adult family members become leaders of FM/MPF classes and are instrumental in expanding the programs. Parents and adult family members, teachers, and aides report the stronger relations between home and school. Parents become advocates for the curriculum. Teachers report increased confidence in their own mathematics understanding and deeper perceptions about their students.

Staff Support: Although workshops and inservices are recommended, the program can be implemented using only the FM/MPF resource book.

(Year initiated: 1989)

NCISE Standards met:

☐ Accessible to all students.

☐ Build on students' prior experience and knowledge.

☐ Use an instructional model based on the scientific process such as: question, discover, create, communicate, and pursue new questions.

☐ Relate to personal and social needs.

☐ Select science concepts that are developmentally appropriate, with illustrative examples drawn from the content of multiple disciplines of science.

☐ Develop scientific thinking skills such as drawing conclusions based on evidence, using inference, creating models.

☐ Develop scientific habits of mind such as curiosity, skepticism, honesty, living with ambiguity.

☐ Use authentic assessments to chart teaching and learning.

☐ Shift the role of teacher from imparter of knowledge to designer and facilitator of learning.

☐ Seek relevant and significant applications of science content and concepts to students' personal and community life.

NCTM standards met:

☑ Pose tasks based on sound and significant mathematics.

☑ Build on students' prior experience and knowledge.

☑ Develop mathematics thinking skills that convince students of the validity of particular representations, solutions, conjectures, and answers.

☑ Engage students' intellect; pose questions and tasks that elicit, engage, and challenge each students' thinking.

☑ Develop students' mathematical knowledge and skills.

☑ Stimulate students to make connections and develop a coherent framework for mathematical ideas.

☑ Call for problem formulation, problem solving, and mathematical reasoning.

☑ Promote the development of all students' dispositions to do mathematics.

☑ Develop an instructional model based on the range of ways students learn mathematics.

RESOURCES/MATERIALS NEEDED FOR ADOPTION:

The FM/MPF books contain the math challenges, other resources, and information on how to organize classes, as well as suggestions for how parents can work with their children. The books themselves are innovative in that they are written to the parents with the intention that they can begin using them immediately with their children.

Equipment Needed:

- Inexpensive household objects
- Curriculum: FM/MPF book

Support Needed:

- Staff Development (recommended)
- Workshop/Inservice (recommended)
- Book

Note: Staff development: costs about $50-75 per team; workshops that cost $100 per person are encouraged, again with pro-rated increases for additional people (+ $50 for each additional team person). Also the program allows families to begin using materials immediately at home without requiring classes. The $15 book is available free as part of the workshop.

FUNDED BY: Carnegie Foundation, U.S. Department of Education, FIPSE (Fund for Improvement of Post-Secondary Education), WEEA

CONTACT:
Mary Jo Cittadino
Network Coordinator
EQUALS/Family Math/IMP
Lawrence Hall of Science
University of California
Berkeley, CA 94720
(510) 642-0738
Fax: (510) 643-5757

SITE(S):

Sites exist in about 30 U.S. states and in Australia, New Zealand, and Costa Rica.

Source: Far West Laboratory

THE KENTUCKY K-4 MATHEMATICS SPECIALIST PROGRAM

University of Kentucky
Lexington, KY

A Staff Development Program for K-4 Math Teachers

TOPIC: Elementary Math

USER(S): K-4 Educators

TARGET POPULATION: All Students

EMPHASIS ON:

Instructional Materials	Teaching Strategies	Assessment Tools
• N/A	• Hands-On Learning	• N/A
	• Student-Centered Learning	
	• Cooperative/Group Learning	
	• Technology-Based Strategies	

GENERAL DESCRIPTION

The program developed a network of K-4 mathematics specialists across Kentucky through a pyramid approach to professional development. Twenty-four exemplary elementary teachers and 24 teacher educators were trained in the hands-on program grounded in the NCTM standards and emphasizing geometry, number sense, measurement, statistics, lesson development, assessment, parent involvement, and conducting workshops. The initial 48 educators then trained elementary teachers throughout the state in a series of regional seminars at each of the state universities.

Innovative Features: The most innovative feature of the program is its staff development design which emphasizes the training of trainers who will train the teachers. In this way, a cadre of teachers are developed who continue to network and develop as professionals.

Goals: The program has three major goals: to establish a comprehensive, statewide network of K-4 mathematics specialists to serve as resource persons; to align Kentucky's K-4 mathematics content and teaching practices with the NCTM standards and Kentucky's Education Reform Act of 1990; and to provide opportunities for communication and collaboration among classroom teachers, school supervisors, teacher educators, and college mathematicians regarding mathematics content and teaching.

Effectiveness: Survey results indicate that there are 435 K-4 mathematics specialists in Kentucky who continue collaboration and influence others in the teaching of mathematics. Eighty percent of Kentucky's public schools and 25 private schools have mathematics specialists on staff, representing 92% of the school districts in the state. Elementary teachers have become actively involved in statewide mathematics education activities. The research/evaluation component of the program (two research teams of university faculty: the micro-research and the macro-research teams) found the results generally positive and indicated that the goals of the program were met.

Staff Support: The program is to be implemented by district or university-level individuals. A series of seminars totaling 45 hours is presented to elementary teachers by a team of exemplary teachers, teacher educators, and mathematicians.

(Year initiated: 1990)

NCISE Standards met:

☐ Accessible to all students.

☐ Build on students' prior experience and knowledge.

☐ Use an instructional model based on the scientific process such as: question, discover, create, communicate, and pursue new questions.

☐ Relate to personal and social needs.

☐ Select science concepts that are developmentally appropriate, with illustrative examples drawn from the content of multiple disciplines of science.

☐ Develop scientific thinking skills such as drawing conclusions based on evidence, using inference, creating models.

☐ Develop scientific habits of mind such as curiosity, skepticism, honesty, living with ambiguity.

☐ Use authentic assessments to chart teaching and learning.

☐ Shift the role of teacher from imparter of knowledge to designer and facilitator of learning.

☐ Seek relevant and significant applications of science content and concepts to students' personal and community life.

NCTM standards met:

☑ Pose tasks based on sound and significant mathematics.

☑ Build on students' prior experience and knowledge.

☑ Develop mathematics thinking skills that convince students of the validity of particular representations, solutions, conjectures, and answers.

☑ Engage students' intellect; pose questions and tasks that elicit, engage, and challenge each students' thinking.

☑ Develop students' mathematical knowledge and skills.

☑ Stimulate students to make connections and develop a coherent framework for mathematical ideas.

☑ Call for problem formulation, problem solving, and mathematical reasoning.

☑ Promote the development of all students' dispositions to do mathematics.

☑ Develop an instructional model based on the range of ways students learn mathematics.

RESOURCES/MATERIALS NEEDED FOR ADOPTION:

A manipulatives kit and the developed resource materials are necessary to support the program.

Equipment Needed:

• Manipulatives

Support Needed:

• Staff Development

• Training Packets

• Workshop/Inservice

• Consultants/Trainers

• Teacher Collaboration/Support Groups

FUNDED BY: National Science Foundation, Eisenhower Mathematics and Science Education Program, State, Exxon Education Foundation

CONTACT:
Dr. William S. Bush, Director
College of Education
305 Dickey Hall
University of Kentucky
Lexington, KY 40506-0017
(606) 257-2927
Fax: (606) 258-1046

SITE(S):
University of Kentucky
College of Education
101 Dickey Hall
Lexington, KY 40506-0017

Source: Appalachia Educational Laboratory

MARIETTA HANDS-ON MATH

Marietta City Schools
Marietta, GA

Hands-On Elementary Math Program

TOPIC: Elementary Math

USER(S): K-5 Educators

TARGET POPULATION: All Students

EMPHASIS ON:

Instructional Materials	Teaching Strategies	Assessment Tools
• N/A	• Hands-On Learning	• N/A
	• Student-Centered Learning	
	• Cooperative/Group Learning	

GENERAL DESCRIPTION

This is a K-5 math program which uses manipulatives to create hands-on concrete experiences in order to teach estimation, analysis, and problem solving to all types of students in regular classrooms.

Innovative Features: Training and materials are supplied to the participating teachers. This assures that the process of integration into the classroom is a natural one.

Goals: The basic goal is to demonstrate that systematic use of concrete manipulative materials during mathematics instruction improves concept development, problem solving, and computation as measured by achievement tests. Two additional objectives are to show that adequately trained teachers armed with proper materials will make a positive difference in mathematics instruction and that students in the classes of those teachers will engage in significantly more hands-on learning activities than will students in a traditional classroom.

Effectiveness: A stringent evaluation, both qualitative and quantitative, has shown significant improvement in students' mathematical abilities.

(Year initiated: 1988)

NCISE Standards met:

☐ Accessible to all students.

☐ Build on students' prior experience and knowledge.

☐ Use an instructional model based on the scientific process such as: question, discover, create, communicate, and pursue new questions.

☐ Relate to personal and social needs.

☐ Select science concepts that are developmentally appropriate, with illustrative examples drawn from the content of multiple disciplines of science.

☐ Develop scientific thinking skills such as drawing conclusions based on evidence, using inference, creating models.

☐ Develop scientific habits of mind such as curiosity, skepticism, honesty, living with ambiguity.

☐ Use authentic assessments to chart teaching and learning.

☐ Shift the role of teacher from imparter of knowledge to designer and facilitator of learning.

☐ Seek relevant and significant applications of science content and concepts to students' personal and community life.

NCTM standards met:

☑ Pose tasks based on sound and significant mathematics.

☑ Build on students' prior experience and knowledge.

☑ Develop mathematics thinking skills that convince students of the validity of particular representations, solutions, conjectures, and answers.

☑ Engage students' intellect; pose questions and tasks that elicit, engage, and challenge each students' thinking.

☑ Develop students' mathematical knowledge and skills.

☑ Stimulate students to make connections and develop a coherent framework for mathematical ideas.

☑ Call for problem formulation, problem solving, and mathematical reasoning.

☐ Promote the development of all students' dispositions to do mathematics.

☑ Develop an instructional model based on the range of ways students learn mathematics.

RESOURCES/MATERIALS NEEDED FOR ADOPTION:

A variety of concrete manipulatives, suitable for a particular grade level must be made available to participating teachers. Included in these would be interlocking cubes, pattern blocks, base-ten blocks, etc.

Equipment Needed:

- Manipulatives

Support Needed:

- Staff Development
- Workshop/Inservice

Note: Support and encouragement from system personnel to make a change.

FUNDED BY: District, State

CONTACT:

SERVE Consortium for Mathematics
and Science Education
345 S. Magnolia Dr., Suite D-23
Tallahassee, FL 32301-2950
(904) 922-8533; (800) 854-0476
Fax: (904) 922-8068

SITE(S):

Marietta City Schools
145 Dodd Street P.O. Box 1265
Marietta, GA 30061
(Program used district-wide)

Source: SouthEastern Regional Vision for Education

MATH 2002

Messiah College
Grantham, PA

Teachers and Student Teachers Work Together to Revise Traditional Math Instruction

TOPIC: Elementary Math

USER(S): K-5 Educators, Student Teachers

TARGET POPULATION: Urban, At-Risk, Ethnic/Minority

EMPHASIS ON:

Instructional Materials	Teaching Strategies	Assessment Tools
• Supplemental Learning/Teaching Materials	• Hands-On Learning	• N/A
	• Student-Centered Learning	
	• Cooperative/Group Learning	
	• Technology-Based Strategies	

GENERAL DESCRIPTION

Math 2002 is a professional development program which pairs regular classroom teachers with inservice student teachers to update traditional mathematics instruction.

Innovative Features: The most significant innovation is the action research process in which the college and its student teachers work to create a climate which supports experimentation, change and results in professional growth for both the student teacher and the classroom cooperating teacher.

Goals: To encourage the use of higher-order thinking skills, appropriate manipulatives, cooperative learning and the use of technology in mathematics instruction. The developers feel that using appropriate curriculum resources and lesson plans encourages attitude changes that favor a life-long interest in mathematics.

Effectiveness: This was measured by informal pre-post surveys on teacher attitudes toward mathematics, calculator use, teaching problem solving, and using technology and manipulatives in the classroom. All attitudes were more positive after participating in the program.

Staff Support: Program is built around inservice both before and during the school year under the direction of the college student teacher supervisor.

(Year initiated: 1991)

NCISE Standards met:

☐ Accessible to all students.

☐ Build on students' prior experience and knowledge.

☐ Use an instructional model based on the scientific process such as: question, discover, create, communicate, and pursue new questions.

☐ Relate to personal and social needs.

☐ Select science concepts that are developmentally appropriate, with illustrative examples drawn from the content of multiple disciplines of science.

☑ Develop scientific thinking skills such as drawing conclusions based on evidence, using inference, creating models.

☐ Develop scientific habits of mind such as curiosity, skepticism, honesty, living with ambiguity.

☐ Use authentic assessments to chart teaching and learning.

☐ Shift the role of teacher from imparter of knowledge to designer and facilitator of learning.

☐ Seek relevant and significant applications of science content and concepts to students' personal and community life.

NCTM standards met:

☑ Pose tasks based on sound and significant mathematics.

☑ Build on students' prior experience and knowledge.

☑ Develop mathematics thinking skills that convince students of the validity of particular representations, solutions, conjectures, and answers.

☑ Engage students' intellect; pose questions and tasks that elicit, engage, and challenge each students' thinking.

☑ Develop students' mathematical knowledge and skills.

☑ Stimulate students to make connections and develop a coherent framework for mathematical ideas.

☑ Call for problem formulation, problem solving, and mathematical reasoning.

☑ Promote the development of all students' dispositions to do mathematics.

☑ Develop an instructional model based on the range of ways students learn mathematics.

RESOURCES/MATERIALS NEEDED FOR ADOPTION:

Materials and curriculum resources such as slates, calculators, unifix cubes, teddy bear counters, science related equipment, cooperative learning materials, and computers as well as printed materials such as literature and science books with math connections for both teachers and students.

Equipment Needed:

- VCR
- Software
- Macintosh Computer
- Manipulatives
- Calculators

Support Needed:

- Orientation
- Technical Assistance
- Training Packets
- Videotapes
- Workshop/Inservice
- Consultants/Trainers

FUNDED BY: Eisenhower Mathematics and Science Education Program

CONTACT:
Dr. Velma Yoder
Project Director
302 Old Main, Messiah College
Grantham, PA 17027
(717) 766-2511, Ext. 7053

SITE(S):
Foose Early Childhood Center
1301 Sycamore Street
Harrisburg, PA 17104

Source: Research for Better Schools

MATHEMATICS EDUCATION INITIATIVE/MOVE IT MATH

University of Houston-Victoria
Victoria, TX

K-6 Hands-on, Discovery Mathematics for ALL Children

TOPIC: Elementary Math

USER(S): K-6 Educators, Curriculum Specialists, School Administrators, College Faculty, Education Consultants, Parents

TARGET POPULATION: All Students

EMPHASIS ON:

Instructional Materials	Teaching Strategies	Assessment Tools
• Supplemental Learning/Teaching Materials	• Hands-On Learning	• N/A
• Teaching Lessons/Units	• Student-Centered Learning	
• Curriculum Guides	• Cooperative/Group Learning	
• Technology-Based Materials	• Technology-Based Strategies	

GENERAL DESCRIPTION

MOVE IT Math is a K-6 university-supported professional development program. It advocates mathematics instruction based on the use of manipulatives. It consists of three 30-hour inservices: Everyone Can Learn Math, Enrichment & Accelerate, and Advanced Topics.

Innovative features: MOVE IT Math includes the following:

1. Immersion in manipulatives until the mathematics being modeled is internalized;

2. introduction to algebra as early as kindergarten;

4. use of children's literature and science to give meaning and purpose to mathematics;

5. attention to mathematics as a language for explaining certain events;

6. emphasis on understanding rather than memorization;

7. students discovery of the "rules" of mathematics through pattern examination;

8. flexibility in its exposition and acceptance of alternative ways to solve problems; and

9. teaching "essential elements," not covering textbook pages.

Goals: MOVE IT Math seeks a balance between skills, concepts, and problem solving in order to: 1. elevate scores on standardized exams; 2. meet the challenge of changing demographics; 3. improve student attitudes toward mathematics and teacher attitudes toward teaching mathematics; 4. mainstream "at risk" students for mathematics; 5. aid "at-risk" students in meeting grade-level expectations; and 6. prepare students to participate in a mathematically literate global economy. An objective of the program is that all children will be ready for a quality algebra class in the 8th grade.

Effectiveness: Data collected in 1989 indicated that approximately 80% of the children classified as at-risk (i.e., one year below grade level in reading and/or mathematics) were no longer classified as such after being in the program for approximately six months. All children in an elementary school tested out of the "Chapter" program for mathematics in 1992-93 after implementing the program. Also, teachers report increased understanding, enthusiasm, and interest in teaching mathematics. In some schools, student attendance and discipline problems have shown marked improvement.

(Year initiated: 1987)

NCISE Standards met:

☐ Accessible to all students.

☐ Build on students' prior experience and knowledge.

☐ Use an instructional model based on the scientific process such as: question, discover, create, communicate, and pursue new questions.

☐ Relate to personal and social needs.

☐ Select science concepts that are developmentally appropriate, with illustrative examples drawn from the content of multiple disciplines of science.

☐ Develop scientific thinking skills such as drawing conclusions based on evidence, using inference, creating models.

☐ Develop scientific habits of mind such as curiosity, skepticism, honesty, living with ambiguity.

☐ Use authentic assessments to chart teaching and learning.

☐ Shift the role of teacher from imparter of knowledge to designer and facilitator of learning.

☐ Seek to find relevant and significant applications of science content and concepts to students' personal and community life.

NCTM standards met:

☑ Pose tasks based on sound and significant mathematics.

☑ Build on students' prior experience and knowledge.

☑ Develop mathematics thinking skills that convince students of the validity of particular representations, solutions, conjectures, and answers.

☑ Engage students' intellect; pose questions and tasks that elicit, engage, and challenge each students' thinking.

☑ Develop students' mathematical knowledge and skills.

☑ Stimulate students to make connections and develop a coherent framework for mathematical ideas.

☑ Call for problem formulation, problem solving, and mathematical reasoning.

☑ Promote the development of all students' dispositions to do mathematics.

☑ Develop an instructional model based on the range of ways students learn mathematics.

RESOURCES/MATERIALS NEEDED FOR ADOPTION:

1. Manipulatives – in particular mathematics balance – multibase blocks and/or counters for trading activities, fraction circles (to support Level 1 inservice).

2. Library of teacher resource materials covering the seven strands from the NCTM Mathematics Standards (to support Level 2 and 3 inservices), estimated cost of $5000, which the district must agree to purchase.

3. Access to a computer in order to access the data base for selecting lessons from the library and to personalize the curriculum to address local student needs.

Equipment Needed:

- Manipulatives
- Computer Equipment
- Special Hands-On Equipment (exchange blocks, fraction cakes)

Support Needed:

- Orientation
- Staff Development
- Training Packet
- Workshop/Inservice
- Consultants/Trainers
- Teacher Collaboration/Support Groups
- Administrative Support

Note: Participants begin with an overview on the need for mathematics reform in the early grades. Workshops are conducted by two trainers who must have used MOVE IT Math in their classrooms for a minimum of one year. Workshops are limited to 35 participants and are supported with a 350-page instructional packet for teachers and an implementation guide for administrators. Teachers receive scope and sequence support materials and the district sponsoring the inservice receives a curriculum database keyed to the essential elements. Four teacher resource books and supporting videos are being produced for Level 1 MOVE IT Math. These materials and additional teacher resource books and videos will be produced for Levels 2 and 3.

FUNDED BY: Eisenhower Mathematics and Science Education Program. Typically, funds provide manipulatives and resource materials used to implement the program with a school or school district paying tuition for three hours of university graduate credit and the University of Houston-Victoria paying for instruction.

CONTACT:

Dr. Paul Shoecraft, Director MEI
Lynne Shoecraft, Assistant Director MEI
University of Houston-Victoria
2506 E. Red River
Victoria, TX 77901
(512) 576-3151; Fax: (512) 572-8463

SITE(S):

Comal Independent School District
1421 Highway 81 East
New Braunfels, TX 78130

Source: Southwest Educational Development Laboratory

MICHIGAN MATHEMATICS INSERVICE PROJECT

Department of Mathematics & Statistics, Western Michigan University
Kalamazoo, MI

Teachers' Inservice Program Upgrades K-6 Mathematics Instruction

TOPIC: Elementary Math

USER(S): K-8 Educators

TARGET POPULATION: All Students

EMPHASIS ON:

Instructional Materials	Teaching Strategies	Assessment Tools
• Teaching Package with Lessons/Units	• Hands-On Learning • Student-Centered Learning • Whole Language Approach • Cooperative/Group Learning	• N/A

GENERAL DESCRIPTION

The **Michigan Mathematics Inservice Project (M²IP)** provides teachers with an opportunity to update mathematics teaching with elementary and middle school children.

The program has been designed and implemented by a statewide project staff. It includes inservice materials to support a two-year inservice program, the preparation of inservice leaders, and the creation of an administrative structure to disseminate the project.

Innovative Features: The main innovative feature of the project is the use of a model consisting of 10 mathematics teaching principles based upon research, new priorities in mathematics education, and the teaching experiences of the project staff. The primary focus of each M²IP session is participation in a model lesson, analysis of the lesson in relation to the Mathematics Teaching Principles, and adaptation of the lesson by grade levels for implementation in the participants' classrooms prior to the next session.

Goals: The primary goal of the project is to improve the mathematics achievement of grades K-6 students through inservice programs for teachers.

Effectiveness: Data suggest that teachers assess their mathematics preparation to be better at the end of the program and that they like mathematics more as a result of the M²IP training. The paired t- tests used to measure these differences were significant at the .01 level.

Staff Support: The program is implemented by K-8 educators and college faculty who have been certified through the M²IP Trainers Program.

(Year initiated: 1989)

NCISE Standards met:

☐ Accessible to all students.

☐ Build on students' prior experience and knowledge.

☐ Use an instructional model based on the scientific process such as: question, discover, create, communicate, and pursue new questions.

☐ Relate to personal and social needs.

☐ Select science concepts that are developmentally appropriate, with illustrative examples drawn from the content of multiple disciplines of science.

☐ Develop scientific thinking skills such as drawing conclusions based on evidence, using inference, creating models.

☐ Develop scientific habits of mind such as curiosity, skepticism, honesty, living with ambiguity.

☐ Use authentic assessments to chart teaching and learning.

☐ Shift the role of teacher from imparter of knowledge to designer and facilitator of learning.

☐ Seek relevant and significant applications of science content and concepts to students' personal and community life.

NCTM standards met:

☑ Pose tasks based on sound and significant mathematics.

☑ Build on students' prior experience and knowledge.

☑ Develop mathematics thinking skills that convince students of the validity of particular representations, solutions, conjectures, and answers.

☑ Engage students' intellect; pose questions and tasks that elicit, engage, and challenge each students' thinking.

☑ Develop students' mathematical knowledge and skills.

☑ Stimulate students to make connections and develop a coherent framework for mathematical ideas.

☑ Call for problem formulation, problem solving, and mathematical reasoning.

☑ Promote the development of all students' dispositions to do mathematics.

☑ Develop an instructional model based on the range of ways students learn mathematics.

RESOURCES/MATERIALS NEEDED FOR ADOPTION:

Project Inservice Packets for Grades K-2; Project Inservice Packets for Grades 3-6; Manipulatives.

Equipment Needed:

- Manipulatives
- Calculators

Support Needed:

- Training Packets
- Workshops/Inservice
- Consultants/Trainers

Note: Trainers of teachers were prepared via statewide M²IP Trainers' programs (40 hours).

FUNDED BY: Chapter II, Eisenhower, District, State, and Eisenhower Higher Education grants have funded the development of materials, evaluation and revisions, and administration of the project standards. Professional Development Funds provided by the State were awarded to prepare trainers.

CONTACT:
Barbara Sandall
North Central Regional Educational Laboratory
1900 Spring Rd., Suite 300
Oak Brook, IL 60521
(708) 571-4700

SITE(S):
Western Michigan University
Kalamazoo, MI 49008

100 Sites in Eaton, Berrien, Colhan County
Intermediate School District

Source: North Central Regional Educational Laboratory

MISTER GOODMATH

Sunrise, FL

Interactive K-8 Math Curriculum Using Closed Circuit Television/Video Tapes and Peer Teaching

TOPIC: Multidisciplinary, Elementary Math, General Math

USER(S): K-5 Educators, Curriculum Specialists, Parents

TARGET POPULATION: All Students

EMPHASIS ON:

Instructional Materials	Teaching Strategies	Assessment Tools
• Technology-Based Materials	• Hands-On Learning	• N/A
	• Student-Centered Learning	
	• Thematic Teaching Approach	
	• Cooperative/Group Learning	

GENERAL DESCRIPTION

The **Mister Goodmath** program consists of a curriculum that makes the teachers and students comfortable with math. It exposes teachers to a wide variety of computational systems and problem-solving strategies not readily found in the district's basal textbooks. These systems and strategies allow teachers to tailor math lessons for students with a diversity of learning styles. The program requires a teacher to assume the role of "Mister Goodmath," a colorful character, who introduces students to a new strategy or idea and challenges a different grade group to a problem of the week. This is done via closed circuit TV, live and taped. Students respond to the problem by writing to Mister Goodmath with not only the answer but also the correct solution. In writing their letters, students must use correct friendly or business letter formats.

Innovative Features: Using the school's closed circuit broadcast TV capabilities, Mister Goodmath appears in live and pretaped programs featuring a variety of math topics. Another innovative feater is peer tutoring by a cadre of high-achieving fifth graders (a.k.a. Goodmath Kids).

Goals: The goal of the program is to offer students as many ways to attack each topic as possible. At the same time, teachers are exposed to math concepts which their methods courses did not cover or they have forgotten.

Staff Support: The administration is committed and has allocated funds to purchase manipulatives and hands-on materials that would strengthen areas of weakness identified on the Iowa Test for Basic Skills. A staff member must become the Mister Goodmath character.

(Year initiated: 1988)

NCISE Standards met:

- ☐ Accessible to all students.
- ☐ Build on students' prior experience and knowledge.
- ☐ Use an instructional model based on the scientific process such as: question, discover, create, communicate, and pursue new questions.
- ☐ Relate to personal and social needs.
- ☐ Select science concepts that are developmentally appropriate, with illustrative examples drawn from the content of multiple disciplines of science.
- ☐ Develop scientific thinking skills such as drawing conclusions based on evidence, using inference, creating models.
- ☐ Develop scientific habits of mind such as curiosity, skepticism, honesty, living with ambiguity.
- ☐ Use authentic assessments to chart teaching and learning.
- ☐ Shift the role of teacher from imparter of knowledge to designer and facilitator of learning.
- ☐ Seek relevant and significant applications of science content and concepts to students' personal and community life.

NCTM standards met:

- ☑ Pose tasks based on sound and significant mathematics.
- ☑ Build on students' prior experience and knowledge.
- ☑ Develop mathematics thinking skills that convince students of the validity of particular representations, solutions, conjectures, and answers.
- ☑ Engage students' intellect; pose questions and tasks that elicit, engage, and challenge each students' thinking.
- ☑ Develop students' mathematical knowledge and skills.
- ☑ Stimulate students to make connections and develop a coherent framework for mathematical ideas.
- ☑ Call for problem formulation, problem solving, and mathematical reasoning.
- ☑ Promote the development of all students' dispositions to do mathematics.
- ☑ Develop an instructional model based on the range of ways students learn mathematics.

RESOURCES/MATERIALS NEEDED FOR ADOPTION:

At least one classroom set of mathematics manipulatives is necessary. These items can be stored on a cart which can be moved easily. Many publishing companies specializing in education materials offer publications that present unique alternatives to problem solving, computation, estimation, etc. Ordering a copy of the Mister Goodmath tape is a must for getting started.

Equipment Needed:

- VCR
- Monitor
- Manipulatives
- Mailbox
- Student Awards
- VHS Camcorder

Support Needed:

- Videotapes: A twenty-two minute awareness video will enable schools to get started. For information, contact Mike Rooney at Welleby Elementary School, 3230 Nob Hill Road, Sunrise, Florida 33351 or phone (305) 572-1210.

FUNDED BY: PTA Funds

CONTACT:

SERVE Consortium for Mathematics and Science Education
345 S. Magnolia Dr., Suite D-23
Tallahassee, FL 32301-2950
(904) 922-8533; (800) 854-0476
Fax: (904) 922-8068

SITE(S):

Welleby Elementary
3230 Nob Hill Road
Sunrise, FL 33351

Source: SouthEastern Regional Vision for Education

SCIENCE
ELEMENTARY GRADES

(**Note:** K-12 programs appear in the *Science: Middle Grades - Post Secondary* section
of this publication, p.93)

NEWTON K-6 SCIENCE PROGRAM

Science Center
Newtonville, MA

Hands-On Science Inquiry into Science Teaches Developmentally Appropriate Concepts & Skills

TOPIC: Elementary Science, Multidisciplinary

USER(S): K-6 Educators, Curriculum Specialists, Science Coordinator

TARGET POPULATION: All Students

EMPHASIS ON:

Instructional Materials	Teaching Strategies	Assessment Tools
• Curriculum Guides	• Hands-On Learning	• N/A
• Supplemental	• Student-Centered Learning	
• Learning/Teaching Materials	• Cooperative/Group Learning	

GENERAL DESCRIPTION

The **Newton K-6 Science Program** is based on a well-articulated, developmentally appropriate matrix of concepts and skills that all students are able to experience. Each year, hands-on experiences are provided in each of four areas of science – plants, animals, earth, and physical science. Since the units are written by staff and by the science coordinator, they reflect the need for diverse activities within a given classroom. Multiple strategies are used for presenting information which enables teachers to engage each child in an appropriate way. This model builds on students' prior experiences while allowing them to construct their own learning.

Goals: The Newton Science Program provides students with experience in differentiating relevant and nonrelevant data, asking and investigating answerable questions, and making the connections needed to learn concepts. Students learn to use various measuring devices such as a thermometer, meter/yard stick, as well as balance and spring scales. Additional work includes constructing and interpreting charts and graphs, and the use of a hand lens, microscope, and other scientific equipment. Students develop attitudes essential to the scientific process including curiosity, creativity, openness to new ideas, and appropriate skepticism. They become able to construct models and to test ideas in order to understand the world around them.

Effectiveness: The program has increased the quality and amount of science being taught, increased teacher participation in professional science activities, and gained support from school administrators and the community. In addition, fourth and eighth grade MEAP scores in the areas of process skills and in earth and physical science have increased.

Staff Support: All units have the same format which provides teachers with the information and strategies necessary to teach the unit. Each classroom teacher has his or her own kit of materials, which is maintained through the Newton's Science Center. Revised units with supporting trade books, technology, and other materials are introduced at teacher-led workshops.

(Year initiated: 1987)

NCISE Standards met:

- ☑ Accessible to all students.
- ☑ Build on students' prior experience and knowledge.
- ☑ Use an instructional model based on the scientific process such as: question, discover, create, communicate, and pursue new questions.
- ☑ Relate to personal and social needs.
- ☑ Select science concepts that are developmentally appropriate, with illustrative examples drawn from the content of multiple disciplines of science.
- ☑ Develop scientific thinking skills such as drawing conclusions based on evidence, using inference, creating models.
- ☑ Develop scientific habits of mind such as curiosity, skepticism, honesty, living with ambiguity.
- ☑ Use authentic assessments to chart teaching and learning.
- ☑ Shift the role of teacher from imparter of knowledge to designer and facilitator of learning.
- ☑ Seek relevant and significant applications of science content and concepts to students' personal and community life.

NCTM standards met:

- ☐ Pose tasks based on sound and significant mathematics.
- ☐ Build on students' prior experience and knowledge.
- ☐ Develop mathematics thinking skills that convince students of the validity of particular representations, solutions, conjectures, and answers.
- ☐ Engage students' intellect; pose questions and tasks that elicit, engage, and challenge each students' thinking.
- ☐ Develop students' mathematical knowledge and skills.
- ☐ Stimulate students to make connections and develop a coherent framework for mathematical ideas.
- ☐ Call for problem formulation, problem solving, and mathematical reasoning.
- ☐ Promote the development of all students' dispositions to do mathematics.
- ☐ Develop an instructional model based on the range of ways students learn mathematics.

RESOURCES/MATERIALS NEEDED FOR ADOPTION:

In addition to the specific units, there are print materials, videos, and technology that enhance the program. Loan materials such Trippensee models should be available to teachers. Living materials are a major component of the program. All of the necessary organisms are easily obtained.

Equipment Needed:

- Special Hands-On Equipment
- Manipulatives
- Living Materials

Support Needed:

- Workshop/Inservice
- Kits/Living Materials Distribution System

FUNDED BY: Eisenhower Mathematics and Science Education Program, District

CONTACT:
Maxine Rosenberg
Science Coordinator K-8
Science Center
100 Walnut Street
Newtonville, MA 02160
(Mail Inquiries Only)

SITE(S):
Newton Public Schools, Newton, MA

Source: The Regional Laboratory for Educational Improvement of the Northeast and the Islands

PROCESS SKILLS ASSESSMENT KITS

Badger Road Elementary School
Fairbanks, AK

Developmentally Appropriate, Hands-On Science Assessment Kits

TOPIC: Elementary Science, Multidisciplinary

USER(S): K-5 Educators

TARGET POPULATION: All Students

EMPHASIS ON:

Instructional Materials	Teaching Strategies	Assessment Tools
• N/A	• N/A	• Student Performance Assessment Materials
		• Fully equipped kits for assessing process skills at each grade level to guide instruction

GENERAL DESCRIPTION

Science Process Skills Assessment Kits provide teachers with developmentally appropriate tasks to assess students' strengths and weaknesses and then plan appropriate hands-on instruction.

Innovative Features: The kits have been carefully articulated from grade to grade to allow a schoolwide outcome-based assessment of science process skills.

Goals: The goal is to continue to improve science teaching by developing an assessment program that is teacher friendly and provides a favorable vehicle for learning.

Effectiveness: Though the kits are still in the pilot phase, informal observation indicates two definite effects. While designing and piloting the kits, the teachers became more aware of science process skills and changed their instruction to include more developmentally appropriate practices.

Staff Support: The program is to be implemented by elementary classroom teachers who need training in the use of the kits and support in planning developmentally appropriate activities to align with the assessments.

(Year initiated: 1992)

NCISE Standards met:

☑ Accessible to all students.

☑ Build on students' prior experience and knowledge.

☑ Use an instructional model based on the scientific process such as: question, discover, create, communicate, and pursue new questions.

☐ Relate to personal and social needs.

☑ Select science concepts that are developmentally appropriate, with illustrative examples drawn from the content of multiple disciplines of science.

☑ Develop scientific thinking skills such as drawing conclusions based on evidence, using inference, creating models.

☑ Develop scientific habits of mind such as curiosity, skepticism, honesty, living with ambiguity.

☑ Use authentic assessments to chart teaching and learning.

☑ Shift the role of teacher from imparter of knowledge to designer and facilitator of learning.

☐ Seek relevant and significant applications of science content and concepts to students' personal and community life.

NCTM standards met:

☑ Pose tasks based on sound and significant mathematics.

☑ Build on students' prior experience and knowledge.

☐ Develop mathematics thinking skills that convince students of the validity of particular representations, solutions, conjectures, and answers.

☑ Engage students' intellect; pose questions and tasks that elicit, engage, and challenge each students' thinking.

☑ Develop students' mathematical knowledge and skills.

☐ Stimulate students to make connections and develop a coherent framework for mathematical ideas.

☐ Call for problem formulation, problem solving, and mathematical reasoning.

☐ Promote the development of all students' dispositions to do mathematics.

☑ Develop an instructional model based on the range of ways students learn mathematics.

RESOURCES/MATERIALS NEEDED FOR ADOPTION:

Fully equipped kits include all materials necessary for assessment and instruction. Teacher's manuals include background and worksheets where necessary.

Equipment Needed:

- Manipulatives
- Special Hands-On Equipment
- Teacher's Manuals

Support Needed:

- Grade-Level Orientation

Note: One teacher from each grade level helped write the assessment kits. It is that teacher's job to train his or her grade-level teachers.

FUNDED BY: Eisenhower Mathematics and Science Education Program and State Funds

CONTACT:

Kit Peixotto
Northwest Regional Educational Laboratory
101 SW Main Street, Suite 500
Portland, OR 97204-3212
(503) 275-9500

SITE(S):

Badger Road Elementary School
P.O. Box 71250
Fairbanks, AK 99707

Source: Northwest Regional Educational Laboratory

SOLD ON SCIENCE

Valley Elementary
Pelham, AL

Elementary Science Laboratory Program Using Prepackaged Kits

TOPIC: Elementary Science

USER(S): K-5 Educators, School Administrators, Parents

TARGET POPULATION: At-Risk, Female Students, All Students

EMPHASIS ON:

Instructional Materials	Teaching Strategies	Assessment Tools
• N/A	• Hands-On Learning	• N/A
	• Student-Centered Learning	
	• Cooperative/Group Learning	
	• Technology-Based Strategies	

GENERAL DESCRIPTION

Sold on Science is an elementary science laboratory program that ensures readily available materials for teachers who direct hands-on discovery learning.

Goals: The objectives of the program are to:

1. increase positive laboratory experiences through activity-oriented lessons,

2. increase emphasis on the process skills of science,

3. present science and technology as problem-solving tools, and

4. develop a positive attitude toward science and technology in all students, especially girls.

Innovative Features: The program makes materials easily accessible for teachers to direct hands-on discovery learning. Kits containing items for specific experiments and observations related to units in the Shelby County Scope and Sequence were planned by Valley Elementary School teachers, prepackaged by parent volunteers, and organized for checkout to all classrooms.

Effectiveness: Teachers report that students look forward to lab days. The Stanford Achievement subscore in science was one stanine higher than the School Ability Index stanine for fourth graders.

(Year initiated: 1991)

NCISE Standards met:

- ☑ Accessible to all students.
- ☑ Build on students' prior experience and knowledge.
- ☑ Use an instructional model based on the scientific process such as: question, discover, create, communicate, and pursue new questions.
- ☐ Relate to personal and social needs.
- ☑ Select science concepts that are developmentally appropriate, with illustrative examples drawn from the content of multiple disciplines of science.
- ☑ Develop scientific thinking skills such as drawing conclusions based on evidence, using inference, creating models.
- ☑ Develop scientific habits of mind such as curiosity, skepticism, honesty, living with ambiguity.
- ☐ Use authentic assessments to chart teaching and learning.
- ☑ Shift the role of teacher from imparter of knowledge to designer and facilitator of learning.
- ☐ Seek relevant and significant applications of science content and concepts to students' personal and community life.

NCTM standards met:

- ☐ Pose tasks based on sound and significant mathematics.
- ☐ Build on students' prior experience and knowledge.
- ☐ Develop mathematics thinking skills that convince students of the validity of particular representations, solutions, conjectures, and answers.
- ☐ Engage students' intellect; pose questions and tasks that elicit, engage, and challenge each students' thinking.
- ☐ Develop students' mathematical knowledge and skills.
- ☐ Stimulate students to make connections and develop a coherent framework for mathematical ideas.
- ☐ Call for problem formulation, problem solving, and mathematical reasoning.
- ☐ Promote the development of all students' dispositions to do mathematics.
- ☐ Develop an instructional model based on the range of ways students learn mathematics.

RESOURCES/MATERIALS NEEDED FOR ADOPTION:

The program can be replicated with much less than the $23,000 Valley received in the AmSouth grant. A classroom with regular tables and shelves for storage are basic needs, but innovative teachers and parents could organize kits to accompany units in the science lab. A fund raiser could provide money for microscopes, dissecting instruments, charts, and models. This program should be directed by a member of the school staff.

Equipment Needed:

- Manipulatives
- Special Hands-On Equipment

Support Needed:

- Orientation
- Staff Development
- Teacher Collaboration/Support Groups

Note: College professors can be used to demonstrate effective science lessons using material in the lab. Also parents can volunteer their services as lab assistants.

FUNDED BY: Amsouth Bank Fund for Educational Excellence

CONTACT:

SERVE Consortium for Mathematics
and Science Education
345 S. Magnolia Dr., Suite D-23
Tallahassee, FL 32301-2950
(904) 922-8533; (800) 854-0476
Fax: (904) 922-8068

SITE(S):

Valley Elementary
310 Opportunity Drive
Pelham, AL 35124

Source: SouthEastern Regional Vision for Education

USING THE OUTDOORS TO TEACH EXPERIENTIAL SCIENCE

N.C. State Museum of Natural Sciences
Raleigh, NC

Science Program Using School Grounds as a Living Lab

TOPIC: Elementary Science, Environmental Studies, Biology/Life Science

USER(S): K-6 Educators, Curriculum Specialists, Program Planners, Education Consultants, Paraprofessionals, Media Specialists

TARGET POPULATION: All Students

EMPHASIS ON:

Instructional Materials	Teaching Strategies	Assessment Tools
• N/A	• Hands-On Learning	• N/A
	• Cooperative/Group Learning	
	• Individualized/Self-Paced Learning	

GENERAL DESCRIPTION

This program enhances the academic performance of all students by developing a site-based model that integrates science curriculum programs with outdoor laboratories. The program selects 10 elementary schools per year and provides a large number of teachers at each of the schools with one year of intensive training on how to utilize their school grounds to teach hands-on science.

Innovative Features: Emphasis is placed on enhancing the school grounds as wildlife habitats through encouraging plantings of native wildflowers, shrubs and trees; providing cover for birds and small mammals; and returning selected mowed areas to maintained meadows or natural sites.

Goals: The goals of the program are to provide teachers and students with basic information, to facilitate experiences with living things, and to develop a school-based plan for using the school grounds as an outdoor living laboratory.

Effectiveness: Effectiveness is determined by an evaluation of this program done by Brenda Evans of the Department of Public Instruction. The DPI evaluation methodology provides both qualitative and quantitative data. Site observations and interviews with teachers, staff, students, the business community, and parents are conducted to supplement the formal assessment of student's achievement and interest.

Staff Support: The lead teachers at each school participate in a week-long summer field institute designed to provide additional hands-on natural science training.

(Year initiated: 1991)

NCISE Standards met:

☑ Accessible to all students.

☑ Build on students' prior experience and knowledge.

☑ Use an instructional model based on the scientific process such as: question, discover, create, communicate, and pursue new questions.

☑ Relate to personal and social needs.

☐ Select science concepts that are developmentally appropriate, with illustrative examples drawn from the content of multiple disciplines of science.

☑ Develop scientific thinking skills such as drawing conclusions based on evidence, using inference, creating models.

☑ Develop scientific habits of mind such as curiosity, skepticism, honesty, living with ambiguity.

☐ Use authentic assessments to chart teaching and learning.

☑ Shift the role of teacher from imparter of knowledge to designer and facilitator of learning.

☑ Seek relevant and significant applications of science content and concepts to students' personal and community life.

NCTM standards met:

☐ Pose tasks based on sound and significant mathematics.

☐ Build on students' prior experience and knowledge.

☐ Develop mathematics thinking skills that convince students of the validity of particular representations, solutions, conjectures, and answers.

☐ Engage students' intellect; pose questions and tasks that elicit, engage, and challenge each students' thinking.

☐ Develop students' mathematical knowledge and skills.

☐ Stimulate students to make connections and develop a coherent framework for mathematical ideas.

☐ Call for problem formulation, problem solving, and mathematical reasoning.

☐ Promote the development of all students' dispositions to do mathematics.

☐ Develop an instructional model based on the range of ways students learn mathematics.

RESOURCES/MATERIALS NEEDED FOR ADOPTION:

Manual of school site hands-on activities.

Objects both living and preserved from the natural world.

Equipment Needed:

- VCR
- Hands-On Equipment

Support Needed:

- Orientation
- Staff Development
- Training Packets
- Workshop/Inservice
- Consultants/Trainers

Note: Program success requires a significant group of teachers with administrative and community support to attend 5-6 training sessions led by a natural science educator specialist.

FUNDED BY: National Science Foundation, District, State

CONTACT:

SERVE Consortium for Mathematics
and Science Education
345 S. Magnolia Dr., Suite D-23
Tallahassee, FL 32301-2950
(904) 922-8533; (800) 854-0476
Fax: (904) 922-8068

SITE(S):

N.C. State Museum of Natural Sciences
P.O. Box 27647
Raleigh, NC 27611

Source: SouthEastern Regional Vision for Education

MATHEMATICS
MIDDLE GRADES – POST SECONDARY

(includes K-12)

ARKANSAS MATH CRUSADE

Arkansas Department of Higher Education
Little Rock, AR

Professional Development (Grades 5-College) for Vertical Connections in Mathematics Instruction

TOPIC: Elementary Math, Algebra I, Algebra II, Geometry, Trigonometry, Calculus

USER(S): 5-12 Educators, College Faculty, Classroom teacher to team with college faculty

TARGET POPULATION: All Students

EMPHASIS ON:

Instructional Materials	Teaching Strategies	Assessment Tools
• Supplemental Learning/Teaching Materials	• Hands-On Learning	• Attitude Surveys/Inventories
	• Student-Centered Learning	• Teacher Reaction Inventories
	• Cooperative/Group Learning	• Portfolios
	• Technology-Based Strategies	• Technology-Based Tools

GENERAL DESCRIPTION

The mission of the **Arkansas Math Crusade** is to help mathematics teachers create successful learning environments for every student, to promote professional growth for teachers involving mathematics content and instructional strategies, and to provide access to math manipulatives and technology in all Arkansas mathematics classrooms.

To achieve this, a fifteen module course was developed based on the NCTM *Curriculum and Evaluation Standards* and the NCTM *Professional Teaching Standards*. The course, "Higher Order Thinking in Mathematics," is offered at eleven universities throughout the state. The materials incorporate manipulatives and calculators to create an active learning environment which is modeled and practiced with teachers in cooperative learning groups.

Innovative Features: A college professor and a public school teacher team teach the course. Teachers in grades five through college participate in the class, working together in learning groups. They are trained with and receive approximately $500 worth of mathematics manipulatives which the principal and superintendent must agree to purchase prior to the teacher being accepted into the program.

Goals: During the course, teachers are expected to practice with their students the concepts and teaching strategies that have been modeled. Full implementation of manipulatives and an interactive student-centered style of instruction is the goal of the program.

Effectiveness: In addition to the semester course, teachers must keep a portfolio showing not only their own progress during the course but also samples of student work from their classroom. Writing samples, photographs, student problem-solving attempts, student models, and group work may be included in the portfolio.

Staff Support: In addition to the semester course, teachers participate in three follow-up sessions during the semester following completion of the course.

(Year initiated: 1991)

NCISE Standards met:

- ☐ Accessible to all students.
- ☐ Build on students' prior experience and knowledge.
- ☐ Use an instructional model based on the scientific process such as: question, discover, create, communicate, and pursue new questions.
- ☐ Relate to personal and social needs.
- ☐ Select science concepts that are developmentally appropriate, with illustrative examples drawn from the content of multiple disciplines of science.
- ☐ Develop scientific thinking skills such as drawing conclusions based on evidence, using inference, creating models.
- ☐ Develop scientific habits of mind such as curiosity, skepticism, honesty, living with ambiguity.
- ☐ Use authentic assessments to chart teaching and learning.
- ☐ Shift the role of teacher from imparter of knowledge to designer and facilitator of learning.
- ☐ Seek to find relevant and significant applications of science content and concepts to students' personal and community life.

NCTM standards met:

- ☑ Pose tasks based on sound and significant mathematics.
- ☑ Build on students' prior experience and knowledge.
- ☑ Develop mathematics thinking skills that convince students of the validity of particular representations, solutions, conjectures, and answers.
- ☑ Engage students' intellect; pose questions and tasks that elicit, engage, and challenge each students' thinking.
- ☑ Develop students' mathematical knowledge and skills.
- ☑ Stimulate students to make connections and develop a coherent framework for mathematical ideas.
- ☑ Call for problem formulation, problem solving, and mathematical reasoning.
- ☑ Promote the development of all students' dispositions to do mathematics.
- ☑ Develop an instructional model based on the range of ways students learn mathematics.

RESOURCES/MATERIALS NEEDED FOR ADOPTION:

Schools must agree to buy a classroom set of materials for each participating teacher. PTAs have raised money for this effort and businesses have donated funds to support the purchases of manipulatives and calculators.

Teachers need access to an overhead projector, appropriate computers that can be used with an overhead display, access to a good professional library which includes the *Arithmetic Teacher* and/or *Mathematics Teacher*, professional journals and other support materials on using manipulatives, calculators, and computers. Software that supports mathematical concepts (such as that offered by Sunburst) or access to the IBM Tool Kit is also required.

Equipment Needed: (Resources)

- IBM Compatible Computer Equipment
- Software
- Special Hands-On Equipment
- Manipulatives
- TI-Explorer Calculator
- TI-81 Graphing Calculator
- *Curriculum and Evaluation Standards for School Mathematics (NCTM)*
- *Professional Teaching Standards for School Mathematics (NCTM)*

Support Needed:

- Workshop/Inservice
- Consultants/Trainers
- Graduate Mathematics Course Credit

FUNDED BY: Eisenhower Mathematics and Science Education Program, District, State

CONTACT:

Suzanne Mitchell
Program Director
114 East Capitol Avenue
Little Rock, AR 72201
(501) 324-9300
Fax (501) 324-9308

SITE(S):

Dr. Jay Graening
Department of Mathematical Sciences
301 Science Engineering Building
University of Arkansas
Fayetteville, AR 72701

Source: Southwest Educational Development Laboratory

COLLEGE PREPARATORY MATHEMATICS PROGRAM

The University of Illinois at Chicago
Chicago, IL

A Cooperative Learning Mathematics Program Developed Through School-University Collaborations

---

TOPIC: Pre-Algebra, Algebra I, Geometry, Algebra II, Trigonometry, Elementary Science

USER(S): 9-12 Educators

TARGET POPULATION: Urban, At-Risk, Ethnic/Minority Students, Female Students

---

EMPHASIS ON:

Instructional Materials	Teaching Strategies	Assessment Tools
• N/A	• Hands-On Learning	• Attitude Survey/Inventories
	• Student-Centered Learning	• Teacher Reaction Inventories
	• Cooperative/Group Learning	• Journals
	• Technology-Based Strategies	

GENERAL DESCRIPTION

The program is a university/high school collaboration that helps potentially successful, but under-represented (minority and female) and at-risk students to succeed in precollege mathematics.

Innovative Features: The use of cooperative small-group work as a primary mode of learning is incorporated into a comprehensive program that includes teacher enhancement; student instruction; and development of a team approach, including in-school counselors, and a significant school-university collaboration.

Goals: The primary goal is to establish and maintain an environment that encourages under-represented and at-risk students to enroll and succeed in precollege mathematics.

Effectiveness: Participants perform better on standardized algebra tests than non-participating peers. More than 80% of the beginning freshman enroll in a third or fourth year of mathematics in their junior year.

Staff Support: The program is implemented by high school mathematics teachers who need training by university staff and ongoing support from counselors, university staff, and peers.

(Year initiated: 1990)

NCISE Standards met:

☑ Accessible to all students.

☑ Build on students' prior experience and knowledge.

☑ Use an instructional model based on the scientific process such as: question, discover, create, communicate, and pursue new questions.

☑ Relate to personal and social needs.

☐ Select science concepts that are developmentally appropriate, with illustrative examples drawn from the content of multiple disciplines of science.

☑ Develop scientific thinking skills such as drawing conclusions based on evidence, using inference, creating models.

☑ Develop scientific habits of mind such as curiosity, skepticism, honesty, living with ambiguity.

☑ Use authentic assessments to chart teaching and learning.

☑ Shift the role of teacher from imparter of knowledge to designer and facilitator of learning.

☑ Seek relevant and significant applications of science content and concepts to students' personal and community life.

NCTM standards met:

☑ Pose tasks based on sound and significant mathematics.

☑ Build on students' prior experience and knowledge.

☑ Develop mathematics thinking skills that convince students of the validity of particular representations, solutions, conjectures, and answers.

☑ Engage students' intellect; pose questions and tasks that elicit, engage, and challenge each students' thinking.

☑ Develop students' mathematical knowledge and skills.

☑ Stimulate students to make connections and develop a coherent framework for mathematical ideas.

☑ Call for problem formulation, problem solving, and mathematical reasoning.

☑ Promote the development of all students' dispositions to do mathematics.

☑ Develop an instructional model based on the range of ways students learn mathematics.

RESOURCES/MATERIALS NEEDED FOR ADOPTION:

The approach is more important than the materials. However where needed, innovative curricular materials such as TIMS, MGM, and the Shell materials (as modified by the California Math 1A project) can be used. Frequent use of calculators and imaginative educational software is imbedded in the curriculum.

Equipment Needed:

• Manipulatives

Support Needed:

• Staff Development

• Consultants/Trainers

• Teacher Collaboration/Support Groups

FUNDED BY: National Science Foundation, Eisenhower, State, Chicago Community Trust

CONTACT:
Barbara Sandall
North Central Regional Educational Laboratory
1900 Spring Rd., Suite 300
Oak Brook, IL 60521
(708) 571-4700

SITE(S):
Senn High School
South Shore High School
Whitney Young High School
Bogan High School
Englewood High School
Lake View High School
Lone Technical High School

Source: North Central Regional Educational Laboratory

THE HAWAII ALGEBRA LEARNING PROJECT

University Laboratory School
Honolulu, HI

Algebra I: A Process Approach

TOPIC: Algebra I

USER(S): 7-12 Educators

TARGET POPULATION: At-Risk, Ethnic/Minority Students

EMPHASIS ON:

Instructional Materials	Teaching Strategies	Assessment Tools
• Self-Contained Program/Packet	• Student-Centered Learning	• N/A
• Teaching Lessons/Units	• Cooperative/Group Learning	
• Textbook with Teacher's Guide	• Problem-Heuristic Approach	

GENERAL DESCRIPTION

The focus of **The Hawaii Algebra Learning Project** alters curriculum and instruction to foster the development of problem-solving processes through the sequencing of Algebraic problem tasks. Class time is spent developing the why and how of algebra. This strategy is driven partly by the problems themselves and partly by the pedagogy. The problem contexts encourage students to explore and investigate the uniqueness of answers and the variety of solution paths. The pedagogy is student-centered, with students and teacher sharing ideas.

Innovative Features: The Hawaii Algebra Learning Project is research-based. It requires changes in the roles of the teacher and the students. Students must explain their thinking, coming up with generalizations, and taking an active role in concept development. The teacher becomes guide and facilitator.

Goals: The goals of the Hawaii Algebra Learning Project are to: (1) develop problem-solving processes such as reversibility, flexibility, and the ability to generalize; (2) provide open-ended inquiry appropriate for individual differences; (3) introduce concepts through problem situations; (4) allow time for the development of understanding of concepts and generalizations; and (5) to reinforce skills over time.

Effectiveness: The effectiveness of the program has been determined by student performance on tests, student interviews, teacher observations, and external evaluation.

Staff Support: Teachers must take a 45-hour course. Some forms of follow-up support such groups of teachers using the materials in the same district or formation of user conferences are also helpful.

(Year initiated: 1991)

NCISE Standards met:

☐ Accessible to all students.

☐ Build on students' prior experience and knowledge.

☐ Use an instructional model based on the scientific process such as: question, discover, create, communicate, and pursue new questions.

☐ Relate to personal and social needs.

☐ Select science concepts that are developmentally appropriate, with illustrative examples drawn from the content of multiple disciplines of science.

☐ Develop scientific thinking skills such as drawing conclusions based on evidence, using inference, creating models.

☐ Develop scientific habits of mind such as curiosity, skepticism, honesty, living with ambiguity.

☐ Use authentic assessments to chart teaching and learning.

☐ Shift the role of teacher from imparter of knowledge to designer and facilitator of learning.

☐ Seek relevant and significant applications of science content and concepts to students' personal and community life.

NCTM standards met:

☑ Pose tasks based on sound and significant mathematics.

☑ Build on students' prior experience and knowledge.

☑ Develop mathematics thinking skills that convince students of the validity of particular representations, solutions, conjectures, and answers.

☑ Engage students' intellect; pose questions and tasks that elicit, engage, and challenge each students' thinking.

☑ Develop students' mathematical knowledge and skills.

☑ Stimulate students to make connections and develop a coherent framework for mathematical ideas.

☑ Call for problem formulation, problem solving, and mathematical reasoning.

☑ Promote the development of all students' dispositions to do mathematics.

☑ Develop an instructional model based on the range of ways students learn mathematics.

RESOURCES/MATERIALS NEEDED FOR ADOPTION:

Student texts and teacher's guide

Equipment Needed:

• Overhead Projector with Screen

Support Needed:

• Workshop/Inservice

Note: Teachers who use the program must complete a 45 hour two-week inservice course to understand the theoretic rationale, philosophy, and research supporting the teaching of problem solving within the algebra curriculum; and to understand the problem-solving processes of reversibility, flexibility, and generalization.

FUNDED BY: National Science Foundation, Eisenhower (Title II/Eisenhower awards for inservice of teachers), McInerny Foundation

CONTACT:

Annette Matsumoto or Lani Abrigana
Math. Dept. Chairperson
University Laboratory School
1776 University Avenue
Honolulu, HI 96822
(808) 956-4988 or (808) 956-6216
Fax: (808) 956-4984

SITE(S):

University Laboratory School
1776 University Avenue
Honolulu, HI 96822
(Used in over 100 schools in 9 states)

Source: Pacific Region Educational Laboratory

INTERACTIVE MATHEMATICS PROGRAM

Interactive Mathematics Program
Emeryville, CA

Four-Year Core Curriculum Integrates Math Concepts from Many Topic Areas into a Problem-Based Math Program for All High School Students

TOPIC: Algebra I, Geometry, Algebra II, Trigonometry

USER(S): 9-12 Educators, College Faculty

TARGET POPULATION: All Students

EMPHASIS ON:

Instructional Materials	Teaching Strategies	Assessment Tools
• Program Packet	• Hands-On Learning	• Student Performance
• Supplemental	• Student-Centered Learning	• Assessment Materials
• Learning/Teaching Materials	• Thematic Teaching Approach	• Program Review Materials
• Thematic Instructional Package	• Whole Language Teaching Approach	• Portfolios
• Teaching Lessons/Units	• Cooperative/Group Learning	
• Technology-Based Materials	• Individualized/Self-Paced Learning	
	• Technology-Based Strategies	
	• Problem-Based Learning	

GENERAL DESCRIPTION

Each unit of the **Interactive Mathematics Program (IMP)** is organized around a central problem or theme. Concepts and skills are learned in the context of the unit's central focus through a variety of routine and non-routine smaller problems.

Innovative Features: IMP emphasizes developing conceptual understanding and making connections. Students work in cooperative groups formed heterogeneously by race/gender/perceived "ability" group (un-tracking). Graphing calculators are used extensively. Assessment is embedded throughout the curriculum, including writing, oral presentations, homework, class work, and group participation

Goals: IMP's major goals are to expand and broaden who learns math, what mathematics is, and how it is taught.

Effectiveness: There has been virtually no attrition in the three original pilot schools through three years of math, and almost all of the students have elected to continue studying math for four years. Teachers say they understand the materials for the first time, view themselves as mathematicians rather than math educators, and also see themselves as learners. Students' confidence increases and enjoyment of math increases as they focus on process, not just answers. In addition, their verbal and written skills improve.

Staff Support: Teachers must transition from the traditional skill-based curriculum to a problem-based and concept-based curriculum through inservice workshops, adequate preparation time, team teaching, and other opportunities to share their experiences.

(Year initiated: 1989)

grade level

K 2 4 6 8 10 12 +

NCISE Standards met:

☐ Accessible to all students.

☐ Build on students' prior experience and knowledge.

☐ Use an instructional model based on the scientific process such as: question, discover, create, communicate, and pursue new questions.

☐ Relate to personal and social needs.

☐ Select science concepts that are developmentally appropriate, with illustrative examples drawn from the content of multiple disciplines of science.

☐ Develop scientific thinking skills such as drawing conclusions based on evidence, using inference, creating models.

☐ Develop scientific habits of mind such as curiosity, skepticism, honesty, living with ambiguity.

☐ Use authentic assessments to chart teaching and learning.

☐ Shift the role of teacher from imparter of knowledge to designer and facilitator of learning.

☐ Seek relevant and significant applications of science content and concepts to students' personal and community life.

NCTM standards met:

☑ Pose tasks based on sound and significant mathematics.

☑ Build on students' prior experience and knowledge.

☑ Develop mathematics thinking skills that convince students of the validity of particular representations, solutions, conjectures, and answers.

☑ Engage students' intellect; pose questions and tasks that elicit, engage, and challenge each students' thinking.

☑ Develop students' mathematical knowledge and skills.

☑ Stimulate students to make connections and develop a coherent framework for mathematical ideas.

☑ Call for problem formulation, problem solving, and mathematical reasoning.

☑ Promote the development of all students' dispositions to do mathematics.

☑ Develop an instructional model based on the range of ways students learn mathematics.

RESOURCES/MATERIALS NEEDED FOR ADOPTION:

IMP teacher and student editions of materials

Equipment Needed:

- Manipulatives
- Computer Equipment (optional)
- IBM Compatible
- Macintosh Computer
- Software
- TI Graphing Calculators

Support Needed:

- Staff Development
- Technical Assistance
- Workshop/Inservice
- Teacher Collaborations/Support Groups
- Extra period for professional development
- Team Teaching When Being Taught the First Time

Note: IMP believes the teachers must be given full support in making the transition from the traditional skill-based curriculum to a problem-based and concept-based curriculum. They need inservice workshops, adequate preparation time, team teaching experience, and other opportunities to share their experiences with others.

FUNDED BY: Eisenhower, San Francisco Foundation, SF State University, EQUALS/Lawrence Hall of Science, UC Berkeley, School Districts, California Dept. of Education, U.S. Department of Education, California Post-Secondary Education Commission (CPEC)

CONTACT:
Linda Witnov
Outreach Coordinator (outside CA)
Interactive Mathematics Program
6400 Hollis St, #5
Emeryville, CA 94608
(510) 658-6400
Fax: (510) 658-8920

SITE(S):
University of California
Lawrence Hall of Science
Interactive Mathematics Program
Berkeley, CA 94720

27 Schools: 20 in California, 7 in six other states

Source: Far West Laboratory

MIDDLE GRADES MATHEMATICS PROJECT

Michigan State University
East Lansing, MI

Program Teaches Complex Mathematical Concepts in Grades 6-8

TOPIC: PTO Elementary Math, General Math, Pre-Algebra

USER(S): 6-8 Educators, Curriculum Specialists, School Administrators, College Faculty

TARGET POPULATION: All Students

EMPHASIS ON:

Instructional Materials	Teaching Strategies	Assessment Tools
• A Self-Contained Program/Packet	• Hands-On Learning	• N/A
• Supplemental Learning/Teaching Materials	• Student-Centered Learning	
• Thematic Instructional Package	• Thematic Teaching Approach	
• Teaching Lessons/Units	• Cooperative/Group Learning	

GENERAL DESCRIPTION

Middle Grades Mathematics Project (MGMP) introduces important mathematics in five 6-8 grade curriculum units which reflect the NCTM standards. It uses an instructional model to promote an atmosphere of problem solving and inquiry in the classroom.

Innovative Features: The use of units to assist teachers in the development of a problem-centered instructional approach which is based on a three-phase format (1) the challenge, (2) the exploration, and (3) the summation stage.

Goals: The primary goal of MGMP is to introduce middle school students to important mathematical concepts which are not normally introduced at this level. Through participation in inservice programs, teachers develop new teaching strategies which facilitate the students' new learning.

Effect: Increased use of the project by a large number of school districts throughout the world prompted the National Science Foundation to provide funds to extend the program to an entire curriculum in the "Connected Mathematics Project."

Staff Support: The program is implemented by grade 6-8 elementary teachers who need orientation and ongoing staff development to internalize the process.

(Year initiated: 1986)

NCISE Standards met:

☐ Accessible to all students.

☐ Build on students' prior experience and knowledge.

☐ Use an instructional model based on the scientific process such as: question, discover, create, communicate, and pursue new questions.

☐ Relate to personal and social needs.

☐ Select science concepts that are developmentally appropriate, with illustrative examples drawn from the content of multiple disciplines of science.

☐ Develop scientific thinking skills such as drawing conclusions based on evidence, using inference, creating models.

☐ Develop scientific habits of mind such as curiosity, skepticism, honesty, living with ambiguity.

☐ Use authentic assessments to chart teaching and learning.

☐ Shift the role of teacher from imparter of knowledge to designer and facilitator of learning.

☐ Seek relevant and significant applications of science content and concepts to students' personal and community life.

NCTM standards met:

☑ Pose tasks based on sound and significant mathematics.

☑ Build on students' prior experience and knowledge.

☑ Develop mathematics thinking skills that convince students of the validity of particular representations, solutions, conjectures, and answers.

☑ Engage students' intellect; pose questions and tasks that elicit, engage, and challenge each students' thinking.

☑ Develop students' mathematical knowledge and skills.

☑ Stimulate students to make connections and develop a coherent framework for mathematical ideas.

☑ Call for problem formulation, problem solving, and mathematical reasoning.

☑ Promote the development of all students' dispositions to do mathematics.

☑ Develop an instructional model based on the range of ways students learn mathematics.

RESOURCES/MATERIALS NEEDED FOR ADOPTION:

Schools will need manipulatives, calculators, and MGMP units

Equipment Needed:

• Manipulatives and special equipment

Support Needed:

• Orientation

• Staff Development

• Teacher Collaboration/Support Groups

Note: Teachers will need orientation and on-going staff development to internalize the process. Teacher collaborations are necessary for networking and sharing information.

FUNDED BY: National Science Foundation

CONTACT:
Barbara Sandall
North Central Regional Educational Laboratory
1900 Spring Rd., Suite 300
Oak Brook, IL 60521
(708) 571-4700

SITE(S):
Quasar School, Milwaukee, WI

Source: North Central Regional Educational Laboratory

NORTHWESTERN STATE UNIVERSITY MIDDLE SCHOOL MATHEMATICS PROJECT

Northwestern State University
Natchitoches, LA

University Inservice Programs Translating the Mathematics Standards through Classroom Implementation

TOPIC: General Math

USER(S): 4-8 Educators, Program Planners, Site Coordinators

TARGET POPULATION: At-Risk, Ethnic/Minority

EMPHASIS ON:

Instructional Materials

- Thematic Instructional Package

Teaching Strategies

- Hands-On Learning
- Student-Centered Learning
- Cooperative/Group Learning
- Technology-Based Strategies

Assessment Tools

- Teacher Journals

GENERAL DESCRIPTION

The Northwestern University Middle School Mathematics Project was developed as a component of LaSIP (Louisiana Statewide Systemic Initiative). Thirty-two middle school teachers participated in a six-week summer program consisting of three courses: Number Sense, Conceptual Algebra, and Quantitative Literacy. The methodology and teaching strategies advocated by the National Council of Teachers of Mathematics were included in the courses.

Innovative Features: In this program a Site Coordinator directs the university faculty as they seek to bring new concepts to the teachers in a manner that can be applied in their classrooms. After a university faculty member introduces a concept, the site coordinator presents a demonstration lesson to illustrate how to bring the concept into the classroom.

Effectiveness: The program's effectiveness is proven in the classroom. Program methods have been successfully replicated, some with unique approaches developed by the teachers. The teachers have developed an independence with the mathematics material and methods for teaching.

Staff Support: After the intensive summer training, participants meet three times a semester in Saturday workshops to share experiences and gain new insights from their peers. They have taken suggestions from the summer and created their own approaches that they share with other teachers. Participants' classrooms are visited regularly by the site coordinator.

(Year initiated: 1992)

NCISE Standards met:

- ☐ Accessible to all students.
- ☐ Build on students' prior experience and knowledge.
- ☐ Use an instructional model based on the scientific process such as: question, discover, create, communicate, and pursue new questions.
- ☐ Relate to personal and social needs.
- ☐ Select science concepts that are developmentally appropriate, with illustrative examples drawn from the content of multiple disciplines of science.
- ☐ Develop scientific thinking skills such as drawing conclusions based on evidence, using inference, creating models.
- ☐ Develop scientific habits of mind such as curiosity, skepticism, honesty, living with ambiguity.
- ☐ Use authentic assessments to chart teaching and learning.
- ☐ Shift the role of teacher from imparter of knowledge to designer and facilitator of learning.
- ☐ Seek to find relevant and significant applications of science content and concepts to students' personal and community life.

NCTM standards met:

- ☑ Pose tasks based on sound and significant mathematics.
- ☑ Build on students' prior experience and knowledge.
- ☑ Develop mathematics thinking skills that convince students of the validity of particular representations, solutions, conjectures, and answers.
- ☑ Engage students' intellect; pose questions and tasks that elicit, engage, and challenge each students' thinking.
- ☑ Develop students' mathematical knowledge and skills.
- ☑ Stimulate students to make connections and develop a coherent framework for mathematical ideas.
- ☑ Call for problem formulation, problem solving, and mathematical reasoning.
- ☑ Promote the development of all students' dispositions to do mathematics.
- ☑ Develop an instructional model based on the range of ways students learn mathematics.

RESOURCES/MATERIALS NEEDED FOR ADOPTION:

1. Commercial materials and hands-on manipulatives utilizing hands-on activities
2. Specially developed materials and manipulatives used during inservice workshops
3. Text that includes the recent changes in instruction recommended by the NCTM *Curriculum and Evaluation Standards*
4. Technology-graphing and TI-12 Explorer calculators

Equipment Needed:

- Computer Equipment
- Manipulatives
- Special Developed Materials
- Purchased Materials
- Hand-Held Calculators

Support Needed:

- Staff Development
- Workshop/Inservice
- Consultants/Trainers
- Community and Political Leaders

Note: Staff development for college faculty was essential in the development and demonstration of effective teaching methodology. The summer inservice and academic year follow-up workshops are an integral part of the program, providing continuing support for sustained change in teacher behavior, which is a primary goal of the program. Community and administrative support are necessary and valuable in the continued implementation of real change for effective teaching and teacher training.

FUNDED BY: National Science Foundation, Eisenhower, State, Louisiana Board of Regents of Colleges and Universities, Louisiana Systemic Initiatives Program (LaSIP)

CONTACT:

Stan R. Chadick
Project Director
Department of Mathematics
Northwestern State University
Natchitoches, LA 71497
(318) 357-5033 or (318) 357-5131
Fax: (318) 357-5599

SITE(S):

Department of Mathematics
Northwestern State University
Natchitoches, LA 71497

Source: Southwest Educational Development Laboratory

A PROBLEM SOLVING APPROACH TO MATHEMATICS INSTRUCTION

Brandon, MS

Middle School Math Program Emphasizing Problem Solving

TOPIC: Pre-Algebra, Algebra I

USER(S): 6-8 Educators

TARGET POPULATION: Honors/Advanced Placement

EMPHASIS ON:

Instructional Materials	Teaching Strategies	Assessment Tools
• N/A	• Hands-On Learning	• N/A
	• Student-Centered Learning	
	• Cooperative/Group Learning	
	• Technology-Based Strategies	

GENERAL DESCRIPTION

This middle-school mathematics program teaches students mathematics through a problem-solving approach.

Students analyze underlying mathematics principles and gain confidence in their math abilities by exploring concepts through manipulatives, games, group activities, application projects, and/or tactual activities. They write about ideas related to mathematics in daily, weekly, and quarterly assignments. Tests include open-ended questions and students analyze test errors and prepare written explanations of those errors.

Goals: Goals are to have students understand underlying mathematics concepts; to have them select and use available tools and technology appropriately; to communicate verbally and write the thought processes used to solve mathematical problems; to develop confidence in their own ability to solve problems; and to transfer mathematics applications to other topics within the course curriculum, other mathematics courses, and other subjects.

Effectiveness: In the pilot year of operation, students taking the Mississippi Subject Area Test in Algebra I posted a significant increase ($p<.05$) in test scores on concepts taught with the problem-solving approach as compared to scores on concepts taught with the lecture and demonstration approach. Students have demonstrated improved ability to select and use appropriate problem-solving strategies, as evidenced by the problem of the week results during each year of the program. Past students indicate that skills learned through the problem-solving approach are retained and applied in future mathematics courses.

(Year initiated: 1991)

NCISE Standards met:

- ☐ Accessible to all students.
- ☐ Build on students' prior experience and knowledge.
- ☐ Use an instructional model based on the scientific process such as: question, discover, create, communicate, and pursue new questions.
- ☐ Relate to personal and social needs.
- ☐ Select science concepts that are developmentally appropriate, with illustrative examples drawn from the content of multiple disciplines of science.
- ☐ Develop scientific thinking skills such as drawing conclusions based on evidence, using inference, creating models.
- ☐ Develop scientific habits of mind such as curiosity, skepticism, honesty, living with ambiguity.
- ☐ Use authentic assessments to chart teaching and learning.
- ☐ Shift the role of teacher from imparter of knowledge to designer and facilitator of learning.
- ☐ Seek to find relevant and significant applications of science content and concepts to students' personal and community life.

NCTM standards met:

- ☑ Pose tasks based on sound and significant mathematics.
- ☑ Build on students' prior experience and knowledge.
- ☑ Develop mathematics thinking skills that convince students of the validity of particular representations, solutions, conjectures, and answers.
- ☑ Engage students' intellect; pose questions and tasks that elicit, engage, and challenge each students' thinking.
- ☑ Develop students' mathematical knowledge and skills.
- ☑ Stimulate students to make connections and develop a coherent framework for mathematical ideas.
- ☑ Call for problem formulation, problem solving, and mathematical reasoning.
- ☑ Promote the development of all students' dispositions to do mathematics.
- ☑ Develop an instructional model based on the range of ways students learn mathematics.

RESOURCES/MATERIALS NEEDED FOR ADOPTION:

Materials and curriculum resources are minimal. Problems are obtainable from various sources, especially the monthly calendar problems in Mathematics Teacher. Manipulatives are available from many sources and many can be teacher-made. Calculators increase the range of applications activities but are not essential to the program.

Equipment Needed:

- Manipulatives

Support Needed:

- Orientation
- Staff Development
- Workshop/Inservice
- Teacher Collaborations

FUNDED BY: South Central Bell Mini Grant

CONTACT:

SERVE Consortium for Mathematics
and Science Education
345 S. Magnolia Dr., Suite D-23
Tallahassee, FL 32301-2950
(904) 922-8533; (800) 854-0476
Fax: (904) 922-8068

SITE(S):

Northwest Rankin Attendance Center
9201 Highway 25
Brandon, MS 39042

Source: SouthEastern Regional Vision for Education

TEACHER ENHANCEMENT THROUGH STUDENT RESEARCH PROJECTS

New Mexico State University
Las Cruces, NM

Developing Mathematical Problem-Solving and Communication Skills through Student Research Projects

TOPIC: Algebra I, Geometry, Algebra II, Trigonometry, Calculus

USER(S): 9-12 Educators, College Faculty

TARGET POPULATION: All Students

EMPHASIS ON:

Instructional Materials	Teaching Strategies	Assessment Tools
• Supplemental Learning/Teaching Materials	• Hands-On Learning	• Student Assessment Materials
	• Student-Centered Learning	• Attitude Surveys/Inventories
	• Thematic Teaching Approach	• Portfolios
	• Whole Language Approach	
	• Cooperative/Group Learning	
	• Individualized/Self-Paced Learning	

GENERAL DESCRIPTION

Teacher Enhancement Through Student Research Projects is a high school mathematics program based on "student research projects," multi-step assignments lasting up to several weeks, which involve diverse problem solving skills. While completing a project, students read, write, and speak mathematics. The project was designed by college faculty and high school classroom teachers who participated in a university program modeling the ideal use of research projects as a teaching/learning strategy. In addition, participants then formed support groups.

Innovative Features: Cooperative group learning is emphasized. Projects enable teachers to target specific weaknesses in their students and to supplement existing curriculum in places where it is deficient. Students focus on the problem-solving process rather than on finding numerical answers. The use of scientific investigation creates a means for developing higher-order thinking skills, and all activities are consistent with the standards of the National Council of Teachers of Mathematics.

Effectiveness: In the Las Cruces Public Schools, the Research Projects have been incorporated into traditional classes. Teachers realized that engaging students in solving complicated problems brought out their best work and encouraged students to demonstrate superior abilities. As a result, teachers soon began making extensive changes in their curriculum. Enthusiasm for teaching and willingness to try new instructional strategies and assessment methods increased.

Staff Support: National Science Foundation and Eisenhower funds have been used to conduct follow-up workshops during which teachers continue to write projects which address the particular needs of their students.

(Year initiated: 1990)

NCISE Standards met:

- ☑ Accessible to all students.
- ☑ Build on students' prior experience and knowledge.
- ☑ Use an instructional model based on the scientific process such as: question, discover, create, communicate, and pursue new questions.
- ☐ Relate to personal and social needs.
- ☐ Select science concepts that are developmentally appropriate, with illustrative examples drawn from the content of multiple disciplines of science.
- ☑ Develop scientific thinking skills such as drawing conclusions based on evidence, using inference, creating models.
- ☑ Develop scientific habits of mind such as curiosity, skepticism, honesty, living with ambiguity.
- ☑ Use authentic assessments to chart teaching and learning.
- ☑ Shift the role of teacher from imparter of knowledge to designer and facilitator of learning.
- ☑ Seek to find relevant and significant applications of science content and concepts to students' personal and community life.

NCTM standards met:

- ☑ Pose tasks based on sound and significant mathematics.
- ☑ Build on students' prior experience and knowledge.
- ☑ Develop mathematics thinking skills that convince students of the validity of particular representations, solutions, conjectures, and answers.
- ☑ Engage students' intellect; pose questions and tasks that elicit, engage, and challenge each students' thinking.
- ☑ Develop students' mathematical knowledge and skills.
- ☑ Stimulate students to make connections and develop a coherent framework for mathematical ideas.
- ☑ Call for problem formulation, problem solving, and mathematical reasoning.
- ☑ Promote the development of all students' dispositions to do mathematics.
- ☐ Develop an instructional model based on the range of ways students learn mathematics.

RESOURCES/MATERIALS NEEDED FOR ADOPTION:

With some experience, teachers can learn to write their own assignments; however, access to a collection of projects to use during the school year is important in the beginning. Also needed is a basic understanding of the mathematics standards. The presence of support groups to share the load of project development can be very helpful. Students Research Projects in Calculus (Mathematical Association of America) – a book of teacher-developed projects and materials is also needed.

Equipment Needed:

- None

Support Needed:

- Orientation
- Teacher Collaboration/Support Groups
- Informational resources and supplemental materials for students
- Workshops to provide basic philosophy and current status of mathematics reform

FUNDED BY: National Science Foundation, Eisenhower Mathematics and Science Education Program

CONTACT:

Dr. Douglas Kurtz
Professor of Mathematics
Department of Mathematical Sciences
New Mexico State University
Las Cruces, NM 88003-0001
(505) 646-1410 or (505) 646-3901 (Dept.)
Fax: (505) 646-6218 (attn. 390)

SITE(S):

Las Cruces High School, Mayfield High School, and Onate High School, Las Cruces, NM

Source: Southwest Educational Development Laboratory

TEACHER TRAINING FOR TECHNOLOGY IN THE MATHEMATICS CLASSROOM

University of Central Arkansas
Conway, AR

Instructional Technology for Algebra Classrooms

TOPIC: Pre-Algebra, Algebra I, Algebra II

USER(S): 7-12 Educators, University Mathematics Educators, School Administrators

TARGET POPULATION: Urban, At-Risk, Suburban, Ethnic/Minority, Rural, Female

EMPHASIS ON:

Instructional Materials	Teaching Strategies	Assessment Tools
• Teaching Lessons/Units	• Hands-On Learning	• Portfolios
• Technology-Based Materials	• Student-Centered Learning	• Technology-Based Tools
	• Cooperative/Group Learning	
	• Technology-Based Strategies	

GENERAL DESCRIPTION

Teacher Training for Technology in the Mathematics Classroom assists school districts and teachers in implementing technologically appropriate mathematics instruction. The project is based on the following:

1. the mathematical reform movement led by the National Council of Teachers of Mathematics

2. the belief that mathematics should be accessible to all students, and

3. the importance of computer accessibility for all mathematics students.

Innovative Features: This project equips mathematics classrooms with computer hardware, software, and supplemental resources. The project breaks with traditional staff development and emphasizes the development of lessons and units by teachers.

Effectiveness: Forty-five Arkansas algebra teachers from 42 school districts have participated in Teaching Technology in the Mathematics Classroom during the past two years. Ongoing evaluation of the project includes site visits to the schools and follow-up discussion sessions.

Staff Support: A two-week intensive summer institute focuses on assisting teachers in using computer hardware and software, developing computer-based curriculum materials, and using appropriate instructional strategies. Past participants are invited to attend three annual follow-up sessions in which teachers collaborate on lessons, receive additional training, and participate in a support system.

(Year initiated: 1991)

NCISE Standards met:

☑ Accessible to all students.

☑ Build on students' prior experience and knowledge.

☑ Use an instructional model based on the scientific process such as: question, discover, create, communicate, and pursue new questions.

☐ Relate to personal and social needs.

☐ Select science concepts that are developmentally appropriate, with illustrative examples drawn from the content of multiple disciplines of science.

☑ Develop scientific thinking skills such as drawing conclusions based on evidence, using inference, creating models.

☑ Develop scientific habits of mind such as curiosity, skepticism, honesty, living with ambiguity.

☑ Use authentic assessments to chart teaching and learning.

☑ Shift the role of teacher from imparter of knowledge to designer and facilitator of learning.

☐ Seek to find relevant and significant applications of science content and concepts to students' personal and community life.

NCTM standards met:

☑ Pose tasks based on sound and significant mathematics.

☑ Build on students' prior experience and knowledge.

☑ Develop mathematics thinking skills that convince students of the validity of particular representations, solutions, conjectures, and answers.

☑ Engage students' intellect; pose questions and tasks that elicit, engage, and challenge each students' thinking.

☑ Develop students' mathematical knowledge and skills.

☑ Stimulate students to make connections and develop a coherent framework for mathematical ideas.

☑ Call for problem formulation, problem solving, and mathematical reasoning.

☑ Promote the development of all students' dispositions to do mathematics.

☑ Develop an instructional model based on the range of ways students learn mathematics.

RESOURCES/MATERIALS NEEDED FOR ADOPTION:

Teachers must have hardware and software available to them in their classroom. Appropriate teacher training must include development of curriculum, as well as instructional strategies and assessment strategies.

Equipment Needed:

• MS DOS Equipment

• Software

• LCD (Light writer)

Support Needed:

• Staff Development

• Technical Assistance

• Workshop/Inservice

• Teacher Collaboration/Support Groups

Note: Two weeks of intensive staff development are required. Technical assistance has been provided to teachers by project staff and project Instructional Microcomputer Project for Arkansas Classrooms (IMPAC).

FUNDED BY: Eisenhower Mathematics and Science Education Program, District, State, Project IMPAC

CONTACT:

Linda K. Griffith
Associate Professor
UCA Box 4912
201 Donaghey Avenue
Conway, AR 72035-0001
(501) 450-5663
Fax: (501) 450- 5208

SITE(S):

Karen Williams
Northside High School
Box 1948
Ft. Smith, AR 72902

Source: Southwest Educational Development Laboratory

MULTIDISCIPLINARY PRACTICES

GRADES K-12

ALGEBRA I/PHYSICAL SCIENCE PROJECT

Lathrop High School
Fairbanks, AK

An Integrated Mathematics/Science Program to Encourage Minority Students

TOPIC: Algebra I, Physical Sciences

USER(S): 9-12 Educators

TARGET POPULATION: Urban, At-Risk, Ethnic/Minority

EMPHASIS ON:

Instructional Materials	Teaching Strategies	Assessment Tools
• N/A	• Hands-On Learning	• N/A
	• Cooperative/Group Learning	

GENERAL DESCRIPTION

Students in the **Algebra I/Physical Science Project** have the opportunity to integrate mathematics and science concepts and applications. A block schedule allows flexibility and attention to individual student needs. Career awareness is an integral part of the program.

Innovative Features: The block scheduling and team approach facilitate the integration of mathematics and science. A two-day summer orientation for students and parents introduces the program. The use of speakers and field trips provides a career awareness feature.

Goals: The program encourages minority students to take college prep mathematics, participate in goal setting, and recognize the importance of mathematics and science in career preparation.

Effectiveness: Students in this program during its first year are now taking a fourth level of mathematics. All students who have continued at Lathrop have taken at least a third level of mathematics. The program has encouraged many minority students to set goals and take challenging courses.

Staff Support: The program is implemented by high school mathematics and science teachers. Additional time for collaborative planning should be made available and support from community resources is helpful.

(Year initiated: 1990)

NCISE Standards met:

☑ Accessible to all students.

☑ Build on students' prior experience and knowledge.

☑ Use an instructional model based on the scientific process such as: question, discover, create, communicate, and pursue new questions.

☑ Relate to personal and social needs.

☑ Select science concepts that are developmentally appropriate, with illustrative examples drawn from the content of multiple disciplines of science.

☑ Develop scientific thinking skills such as drawing conclusions based on evidence, using inference, creating models.

☑ Develop scientific habits of mind such as curiosity, skepticism, honesty, living with ambiguity.

☑ Use authentic assessments to chart teaching and learning.

☑ Shift the role of teacher from imparter of knowledge to designer and facilitator of learning.

☑ Seek relevant and significant applications of science content and concepts to students' personal and community life.

NCTM standards met:

☑ Pose tasks based on sound and significant mathematics.

☑ Build on students' prior experience and knowledge.

☑ Develop mathematics thinking skills that convince students of the validity of particular representations, solutions, conjectures, and answers.

☑ Engage students' intellect; pose questions and tasks that elicit, engage, and challenge each students' thinking.

☑ Develop students' mathematical knowledge and skills.

☑ Stimulate students to make connections and develop a coherent framework for mathematical ideas.

☑ Call for problem formulation, problem solving, and mathematical reasoning.

☑ Promote the development of all students' dispositions to do mathematics.

☑ Develop an instructional model based on the range of ways students learn mathematics.

RESOURCES/MATERIALS NEEDED FOR ADOPTION:

The Introductory Physical Science program (IPS). Business and community members active in science and mathematics careers.

Equipment Needed:

• N/A

Support Needed:

• Teacher Collaborations/Support Groups

FUNDED BY: District

CONTACT:

Kit Peixotto
Northwest Regional Educational Laboratory
101 SW Main Street, Suite 500
Portland, OR 97204-3212
(503) 275-9500

SITE(S):

Lathrop High School
901 Airport Way
Fairbanks, AK 99701

Source: Northwest Regional Educational Laboratory

BOCES Outdoor/Environmental Education Program

Smithtown, NY

Cooperative Program Integrates Environmental Issues with Academic Subjects that Help Students Align Their Lives with the Natural World

TOPIC: Multidisciplinary Studies, Elementary Math, General Math, Geometry, Elementary Science, Environmental Studies, Biology/Life Science, Earth/Space Science

USER(S): K-12 Educators, Curriculum Specialists, College Faculty, Educational Consultants, Parents

TARGET POPULATION: All Students

EMPHASIS ON:

Instructional Materials	Teaching Strategies	Assessment Tools
• N/A	• Hands-On Learning	• N/A
	• Student-Centered Learning	
	• Thematic Teaching Approach	
	• Cooperative/Group Learning	

GENERAL DESCRIPTION

BOCES III Outdoor/Environmental Education Program integrates environmental issues with academic subjects in an experiential learning approach.

Innovative Features: The O/EEP is comprehensive, enhances cooperative ventures with other agencies, and is consumer oriented. The programs range from a simple introduction to nature to mentored international research expeditions. Students formulate models, learn to use scientific equipment, relate findings to current knowledge, and draw conclusions.

Goals: The primary goal is to improve academic learning for school-age children while helping preserve nature. The O/EEP uses the natural world in an interdisciplinary approach to teaching, and prepares children to live responsibly with the Earth's natural systems.

Effectiveness: The program is evaluated through student testing and parent/teacher questionnaires. Curricula are evaluated for improving specific, testable thinking skills such as observing, predicting, classifying, and formulating hypotheses. Affective data is collected from verbal feedback and questionnaires from teachers, parents, and staff.

Staff Support: O/EEP's goal-oriented staff development enables teachers to plan for and conduct their own environmental education programs.

(Year initiated: 1971)

NCISE Standards met:

☑ Accessible to all students.

☑ Build on students' prior experience and knowledge.

☑ Use an instructional model based on the scientific process such as: question, discover, create, communicate, and pursue new questions.

☐ Relate to personal and social needs.

☑ Select science concepts that are developmentally appropriate, with illustrative examples drawn from the content of multiple disciplines of science.

☑ Develop scientific thinking skills such as drawing conclusions based on evidence, using inference, creating models.

☑ Develop scientific habits of mind such as curiosity, skepticism, honesty, living with ambiguity.

☐ Use authentic assessments to chart teaching and learning.

☑ Shift the role of teacher from imparter of knowledge to designer and facilitator of learning.

☑ Seek relevant and significant applications of science content and concepts to students' personal and community life.

NCTM standards met:

☑ Pose tasks based on sound and significant mathematics.

☑ Build on students' prior experience and knowledge.

☐ Develop mathematics thinking skills that convince students of the validity of particular representations, solutions, conjectures, and answers.

☑ Engage students' intellect; pose questions and tasks that elicit, engage, and challenge each students' thinking.

☑ Develop students' mathematical knowledge and skills.

☐ Stimulate students to make connections and develop a coherent framework for mathematical ideas.

☑ Call for problem formulation, problem solving, and mathematical reasoning.

☑ Promote the development of all students' dispositions to do mathematics.

☐ Develop an instructional model based on the range of ways students learn mathematics.

RESOURCES/MATERIALS NEEDED FOR ADOPTION:

Natural areas are important to conducting nature studies, but they are not essential to outdoor education or environmental education. There are several excellent models for outdoor education in urban environments. Equipment for lab, field, and classroom studies is also needed: field and lab microscopes, hand lenses, microprojectors, binoculars and spotting scopes, culture dishes, test tubes, Secchi discs, soil analysis equipment, magnets, thermometers, anemometers, compasses, trundle wheels, measuring tapes, scales, photographic enlargers, developing equipment, tape recorders, VCR's and projectors, shovels, trowels, clam rakes, plankton and seine nets, increment borers, chest-waders, life-jackets, gloves, boots, knapsacks, field guides, reference books, art supplies, canoes, and a motorboat.

Curricula such as Outdoor Biological Instructional Strategies, Project Learning Tree, Project Wild, and Long Island Water Resources Curriculum guides.

Equipment Needed:

- Special Hands-On Equipment
- Field and Lab Equipment

Support Needed:

- Orientation
- Staff Development
- Technical Assistance
- Training Packets
- Workshop/In-Service
- Consultant/Trainers

Note: Support services generally entail teacher training, as teachers are the main implementors of the Day-Use program. Our staff provides teachers with orientation, training in outdoor education curricula and methods, technical assistance, and training packets that contain hundreds of instructional activities supplementing traditional subject areas. We use consultants when specialized knowledge is needed or to supplement existing staff.

FUNDED BY: District, State, Federal, Corporate, Institute of Museum Services, SCOPE (Suffolk County Organization for the Promotion of Education)

CONTACT:
Edward J. Zero, Program Administrator
BOCES III Outdoor/Environmental Education Program
Box 604
Smithtown, NY 11787
(Mail Inquiries Only)

SITE(S):
Suffolk County, NY and Other Upstate NY School Districts

Source: The Regional Laboratory for Educational Improvement of the Northeast and the Islands

BOSTON PUBLIC SCHOOLS RECYCLE CENTER

Institute for Self Active Education/National Schools Recycle Center Network
Boston, MA

Center Provides Teachers with Free Materials for Hands-On Learning in Math & Science

TOPIC: Elementary Math, General Math, Geometry, Elementary Science, Environmental Studies, Physics Earth/Space Science

USER(S): K-12 Educators, Curriculum Specialists, School Administrators, State Policymakers, Program Planners, Technology Specialists, College Faculty, Parents, Researchers, Paraprofessionals, Media Specialists, Program Evaluators, State/Federal Administrators

TARGET POPULATION: All Students

EMPHASIS ON:

Instructional Materials	Teaching Strategies	Assessment Tools
• Supplemental Learning/Teaching Materials	• Hands-On Learning	• N/A
• Thematic Instructional Package	• Student-Centered Learning	
• Teaching Lessons/Units	• Thematic Teaching Approach	
• Curriculum Guides	• Whole Language Approach	
	• Cooperative/Group Learning	
	• Individualized/Self-Paced Learning	

GENERAL DESCRIPTION

The Recycle Center distributes material resources to teachers using hands-on approaches for quality mathematics and science education.

The Recycle Center fosters unique business-education partnerships by donating unused by-products, overruns, and rejects for use in stimulating learning activities.

Goals: The project's aim is to:

1. supply an on-going flow of unique and stimulating materials free of charge to teachers,
2. provide inspiring professional development workshops focused on innovative instructional strategies,
3. promote business-school partnerships,
4. divert the flow of reusable materials from landfills and into the hands of teachers and children,
5. serve as a model for development of other Recycle Centers, and
6. promote an ethic of conservation and reuse of valuable materials.

Effectiveness: During the 1991-1992 school year more than 6,187 teachers visited the center. Over $1,000,000 worth of manipulative resources were distributed free to teachers for hands-on mathematics and science activities. The Boston program, with four satellite centers, serves as a model for an emerging National Schools Recycle Center Network.

Staff Support: Sixty-three K-12 workshops were conducted on the creative use of materials.

(Year initiated: 1981)

NCISE Standards met:

☑ Accessible to all students.

☑ Build on students' prior experience and knowledge.

☑ Use an instructional model based on the scientific process such as: question, discover, create, communicate, and pursue new questions.

☑ Relate to personal and social needs.

☑ Select science concepts that are developmentally appropriate, with illustrative examples drawn from the content of multiple disciplines of science.

☑ Develop scientific thinking skills such as drawing conclusions based on evidence, using inference, creating models.

☑ Develop scientific habits of mind such as curiosity, skepticism, honesty, living with ambiguity.

☑ Use authentic assessments to chart teaching and learning.

☑ Shift the role of teacher from imparter of knowledge to designer and facilitator of learning.

☑ Seek relevant and significant applications of science content and concepts to students' personal and community life.

NCTM standards met:

☑ Pose tasks based on sound and significant mathematics.

☑ Build on students' prior experience and knowledge.

☑ Develop mathematics thinking skills that convince students of the validity of particular representations, solutions, conjectures, and answers.

☑ Engage students' intellect; pose questions and tasks that elicit, engage, and challenge each students' thinking.

☑ Develop students' mathematical knowledge and skills.

☑ Stimulate students to make connections and develop a coherent framework for mathematical ideas.

☑ Call for problem formulation, problem solving, and mathematical reasoning.

☑ Promote the development of all students' dispositions to do mathematics.

☑ Develop an instructional model based on the range of ways students learn mathematics.

RESOURCES/MATERIALS NEEDED FOR ADOPTION:

Materials/curriculum resources necessary are provided by business and industry.

Curriculum resource guides are developed by teachers and other curriculum specialists.

Equipment Needed:

- VCR
- Manipulatives
- Storage Space
- Use of a Truck/Van for Collection

Support Needed:

- Orientation
- Technical Assistance
- Training Packets
- Videotapes
- Workshop/In-Service
- Consultant/Trainers

Note: Implementation is achieved by information dissemination using video and printed material, workshops showing and using materials, and follow-up technical assistance on how to create school-based recycle centers. A Program manual is available.

FUNDED BY: Chapter 1, Eisenhower Mathematics and Science Education Program, District, State

CONTACT:
Walter F. Drew, Ed.D., Founding Director
PO Box 1741
Institute for Self Active Education/National
Schools Recycle Center Network
Boston, MA 02205
(Fax or Mail Inquiries Only)
Fax: (407) 984-1018

SITE(S):

Serving all Boston Public Schools, other public and private schools, day care centers, Head Start programs, and neighborhood and community organizations

Source: The Regional Laboratory for Educational Improvement of the Northeast and the Islands

CROSS CURRICULAR MULTI-ABILITY INTEGRATION OF ENVIRONMENTAL EDUCATION

Selah Middle School
Selah, WA

Multi-Age, Multi-Ability Hands-On Environmental Science

TOPIC: Multidisciplinary, Environmental Studies, Biology/Life Science, Physical Sciences

USER(S): 6-8 Educators

TARGET POPULATION: At-Risk, Suburban, Honors/Advanced Placement, Learning Disabled, Emotionally Handicapped

EMPHASIS ON:

Instructional Materials

- Supplemental Learning/ Teaching Materials
- Thematic Instructional Package
- Teaching Lessons/Units

Teaching Strategies

- Hands-On Learning
- Student-Centered Learning
- Thematic Teaching Approach
- Cooperative/Group Learning

Assessment Tools

- Student Performance Assessment Materials
- Attitude Surveys/Inventories
- Program Review Materials
- Exhibits
- Journals

GENERAL DESCRIPTION

The program integrates students from multi-grades and multi-abilities into cooperative teams to conduct field work, complete a variety of classroom tasks, and develop products in the area of environmental education.

Innovative Features: The program incorporates students of varying abilities and needs into cross-grade level groups in order to promote diversity of thought and skills. The program was developed through the collaborative effort of teachers, college professors and scientists.

Goals: The program's two main goals are to provide students with the understanding that they are stewards of the environment and to foster a sense of respect and value for all team members.

Effectiveness: Data from observations, journal writings, and other assessment tools show that students are developing an understanding of the major environmental concepts presented through the project experiences. Students work cooperatively and effectively in multi-age and multi-ability groups. They demonstrate an interest in their environment and an understanding of important issues.

Staff Support: The program is implemented by middle school teachers through collaborative planning. Materials, equipment, and advice from state and local scientists and environmental specialists are desirable.

(Year initiated: 1992)

NCISE Standards met:

☑ Accessible to all students.

☑ Build on students' prior experience and knowledge.

☑ Use an instructional model based on the scientific process such as: question, discover, create, communicate, and pursue new questions.

☑ Relate to personal and social needs.

☑ Select science concepts that are developmentally appropriate, with illustrative examples drawn from the content of multiple disciplines of science.

☑ Develop scientific thinking skills such as drawing conclusions based on evidence, using inference, creating models.

☑ Develop scientific habits of mind such as curiosity, skepticism, honesty, living with ambiguity.

☑ Use authentic assessments to chart teaching and learning.

☑ Shift the role of teacher from imparter of knowledge to designer and facilitator of learning.

☑ Seek relevant and significant applications of science content and concepts to students' personal and community life.

NCTM standards met:

☑ Pose tasks based on sound and significant mathematics.

☑ Build on students' prior experience and knowledge.

☐ Develop mathematics thinking skills that convince students of the validity of particular representations, solutions, conjectures, and answers.

☑ Engage students' intellect; pose questions and tasks that elicit, engage, and challenge each students' thinking.

☐ Develop students' mathematical knowledge and skills.

☐ Stimulate students to make connections and develop a coherent framework for mathematical ideas.

☐ Call for problem formulation, problem solving, and mathematical reasoning.

☐ Promote the development of all students' dispositions to do mathematics.

☐ Develop an instructional model based on the range of ways students learn mathematics.

RESOURCES/MATERIALS NEEDED FOR ADOPTION:

For the fisheries component, student teams need to be equipped with materials appropriate for field work in streams. Background texts or materials on stream water quality, salmon habitat, etc. are also necessary. These materials and resources can be obtained from a variety of sources such as water treatment plants, the Bonneville Power Administration, or U.S.G.S. The global change study was supported by a variety of materials including "Clean Air Washington" from the Department of Ecology, and "Global Warming and the Greenhouse Effect" from GEMS.

Equipment Needed:

• VCR Monitor

• Special Hands-On Equipment

• Water test Kits

Support Needed:

• Staff Development

• Technical Assistance

• Training Packets

• Videotapes

• Workshop/Inservice

• Consultants/Trainers

• Teacher Collaborations/Support Groups

Note: Members of our staff attended the Science Enhancement for Teachers program at the University of Washington to gain background on the topic of global change. Also needed are training and materials to conduct the studies in the fisheries project.

FUNDED BY: The Science Enhancement for Teachers program at the University of Washington.

CONTACT:
Midge Yergen
Science Teacher/Dept. Chair
Selah Middle School
411 North 1st Street
Selah, WA 98942
(Mail Inquiries Only)

SITE(S):
Selah Middle School
411 North 1st Street
Selah, WA 98942

Source: Northwest Regional Educational Laboratory

DEVELOPMENTAL APPROACHES IN SCIENCE AND HEALTH (DASH)

University of Hawaii
Honolulu, HI

DASH: A K-6 Developmental Approaches Science and Health Program

TOPIC: Elementary Science, Environmental Studies, Biology/Life Science, Physics, Earth/Space Science, Chemistry, Health, Technology

USER(S): K-6 Educators

TARGET POPULATION: Urban, At-Risk, Suburban, Ethnic/Minority, Rural, Gifted, Female, Male

EMPHASIS ON:

Instructional Materials

- Self-Contained Program/Packet
- Supplemental Learning/Teaching Materials
- Thematic Instructional Package
- Teaching Lessons/Units
- Videotapes for Follow-Up Inservice

Teaching Strategies

- Hands-On Learning
- Student-Centered Learning
- Thematic Teaching Approach
- Whole Language Approach
- Cooperative/Group Learning

Assessment Tools

- Student Assessment Materials
- Teacher Reaction Inventories
- Portfolios
- Computer Evaluations of Program Workshops

GENERAL DESCRIPTION

The K-6 **DASH** program (developed at the University of Hawaii) integrates learning in science, health and technology, facilitating the use of skills and knowledge of science, health, and technology in both a personal and social context.

Innovative Features: DASH is a true constructivist curriculum where students make their own knowledge out of their own research. DASH involves students in self-evaluation, advocates that teachers use portfolio-based judgment of student progress, and builds on cooperative learning in a heterogeneous classroom. It has a strong environmental component involving students about 30% of their time in environmentally associated studies.

Goals: DASH goals are to facilitate learning of the basic concepts of science, health, and technology in both personal and social contexts, and to develop a commitment to care and nurture our environment and the human community.

Effectiveness: In the fall of 1992 DASH was used by over 100,000 children in grades K-6 in Hawaii, 18 other states of the U.S., and in Australia and New Zealand. DASH has been approved as a validated program of the National Diffusion Network. (After its selection for this publication)

Staff Support: A two-week teacher institute and follow-up inservice are required.

(Year initiated: 1989)

NCISE Standards met:

☑ Accessible to all students.

☑ Build on students' prior experience and knowledge.

☑ Use an instructional model based on the scientific process such as: question, discover, create, communicate, and pursue new questions.

☑ Relate to personal and social needs.

☑ Select science concepts that are developmentally appropriate, with illustrative examples drawn from the content of multiple disciplines of science.

☑ Develop scientific thinking skills such as drawing conclusions based on evidence, using inference, creating models.

☑ Develop scientific habits of mind such as curiosity, skepticism, honesty, living with ambiguity.

☑ Use authentic assessments to chart teaching and learning.

☑ Shift the role of teacher from imparter of knowledge to designer and facilitator of learning.

☑ Seek relevant and significant applications of science content and concepts to students' personal and community life.

NCTM standards met:

☐ Pose tasks based on sound and significant mathematics.

☐ Build on students' prior experience and knowledge.

☐ Develop mathematics thinking skills that convince students of the validity of particular representations, solutions, conjectures, and answers.

☐ Engage students' intellect; pose questions and tasks that elicit, engage, and challenge each students' thinking.

☐ Develop students' mathematical knowledge and skills.

☐ Stimulate students to make connections and develop a coherent framework for mathematical ideas.

☐ Call for problem formulation, problem solving, and mathematical reasoning.

☐ Promote the development of all students' dispositions to do mathematics.

☐ Develop an instructional model based on the range of ways students learn mathematics.

RESOURCES/MATERIALS NEEDED FOR ADOPTION:

Teacher's Guide

Focus Books - single concepts in Big Book or comic format

Reference Library

Blackline Masters

Equipment Needed:

• N/A

Support Needed:

• Training Packets

• Videotapes (Videotapes are used in inservice follow-up sessions.)

• Workshop/Inservice

• Consultants/Trainers

Note: The project requires that teachers using DASH materials attend a ten-day teacher institute. Workshops are taught by an instructional staff of expert DASH teachers who have undergone further instruction to become staff members. The system is supported by special instructors guides. Teachers are certified to teach each grade level for which they receive instruction.

FUNDED BY: State of Hawaii Department of Business & Economic Development & Tourism, National Science Foundation, University of Hawaii, Buhl Science Foundation

CONTACT:

Francis M. Pottenger
Professor of Education
1776 University Ave, UHS 2-202
Honolulu, HI 96822
(808) 956-6918
Fax: (808)-9486

SITE(S):

Judith R. Hallinen
Project Coordinator
Children's School, Carnegie Mellon, MMCC 17
Pittsburgh, PA 15213
(412) 268-1498

(This program is being used in 2000+ schools)

Source: Pacific Region Educational Laboratory

FOUNDATIONAL APPROACHES IN SCIENCE TEACHING (FAST)

University of Hawaii
Honolulu, HI

FAST: A Hands-On Interdisciplinary, Environmental Science Program

TOPIC: Biology/Life Science, Physics, Earth/Space Science, Chemistry, Environmental Studies

USER(S): 6-10 Educators

TARGET POPULATION: All Students

EMPHASIS ON:

Instructional Materials

- Self-Contained Program/Packet
- Supplemental Learning/Teaching Materials
- Technology-Based Materials

Teaching Strategies

- Hands-On Learning
- Student-Centered Learning
- Thematic Teaching Approach
- Cooperative/Group Learning
- Technology-Based Strategies

Assessment Tools

- Student Assessment Materials
- Teacher Reaction Inventories
- Program Review Materials
- Technology-Based Tools

GENERAL DESCRIPTION

The **FAST** program is an interdisciplinary, environmental science program which emphasizes basic concepts and methods of the physical, biological, and earth sciences and relates these to the practical issues of human use of the environment. FAST is designed for students in grades 6-10.

Innovative Features: The FAST program is a true constructivist curriculum where students make their own knowledge out of their own research. It involves students about 70% to 80% of their time in active investigation, linking their findings to the practical societal world. FAST provides opportunities for mathematically adept students to reinforce and expand their skills while helping mathematically struggling students to perform quantitative analysis through graphic means.

FAST assumes that every child builds a unique understanding of the world, which is normalized through teaching; that in science and technology a successful path to normalization is found in reliving the generation of seminal ideas, techniques, and inventions; and that the content and inquiry reflect the nature of the disciplines and technologies being studied.

Effectiveness: In the the fall of 1992 FAST was being used by some 450,000 students in Hawaii, the mainland US, the Pacific islands, and 7 foreign countries. FAST has been in the National Diffusion Network since 1982.

Staff Support: A two-week teacher institute is required.

(Year initiated: 1982)

NCISE Standards met:

- ☑ Accessible to all students.
- ☑ Build on students' prior experience and knowledge.
- ☑ Use an instructional model based on the scientific process such as: question, discover, create, communicate, and pursue new questions.
- ☑ Relate to personal and social needs.
- ☑ Select science concepts that are developmentally appropriate, with illustrative examples drawn from the content of multiple disciplines of science.
- ☑ Develop scientific thinking skills such as drawing conclusions based on evidence, using inference, creating models.
- ☑ Develop scientific habits of mind such as curiosity, skepticism, honesty, living with ambiguity.
- ☑ Use authentic assessments to chart teaching and learning.
- ☑ Shift the role of teacher from imparter of knowledge to designer and facilitator of learning.
- ☑ Seek relevant and significant applications of science content and concepts to students' personal and community life.

NCTM standards met:

- ☐ Pose tasks based on sound and significant mathematics.
- ☐ Build on students' prior experience and knowledge.
- ☐ Develop mathematics thinking skills that convince students of the validity of particular representations, solutions, conjectures, and answers.
- ☐ Engage students' intellect; pose questions and tasks that elicit, engage, and challenge each students' thinking.
- ☐ Develop students' mathematical knowledge and skills.
- ☐ Stimulate students to make connections and develop a coherent framework for mathematical ideas.
- ☐ Call for problem formulation, problem solving, and mathematical reasoning.
- ☐ Promote the development of all students' dispositions to do mathematics.
- ☐ Develop an instructional model based on the range of ways students learn mathematics.

RESOURCES/MATERIALS NEEDED FOR ADOPTION:

Student Book

Reference Booklet Library

Evaluation Guide

Instructional Guide

Equipment Building Kit

Equipment Needed:

- Standard Middle School Laboratory Equipment

Support Needed:

- Staff Development
- Training Packets
- Workshop/Inservice
- Consultants/Trainers

Note: The FAST project requires that for each of the three levels of the program that all teachers attend a 60-hour workshop. Institutes are taught by an instructional staff of expert FAST teachers who have themselves undergone further instruction to become staff members. The institute is supported by a special instructor's guide.

FUNDED BY: University of Hawaii

CONTACT:

Donald B. Young, Associate Professor
1776 University Avenue, CM117
Honolulu, HI 96822
(808) 956-7863
Fax: (808) 956-9486

SITE(S):

43 Demonstration Sites Nationwide Including:
University Laboratory School
University of Hawaii
1776 University Ave.
Honolulu, HI 96822
(808) 956-7833

Source: Pacific Region Educational Laboratory

HANDS-ON ENVIRONMENT

Albert Benjamin Chandler Elementary
Corydon, KY

Primary Grades Environmental Studies Program Using Outdoor Lab

TOPIC: Elementary Math, Elementary Science, Environmental Studies, Biology/Life Science

USER(S): K-4 Educators, School Administrators, Curriculum Specialists, Educational Consultants, Parents, Paraprofessionals, Media Specialists, Program Evaluators

TARGET POPULATION: Rural, Emotionally Handicapped, At-Risk, Ethnic/Minority, Gifted, Learning Disabled

---

EMPHASIS ON:

Instructional Materials	Teaching Strategies	Assessment Tools
• N/A	• Hands-On Learning	• N/A
	• Student-Centered Learning	
	• Thematic Teaching Approach	
	• Whole Language Teaching Approach	
	• Cooperative/Group Learning	
	• Individualized/Self-Paced Learning	

GENERAL DESCRIPTION

Sixty acres of land around Chandler Elementary School is the focus for a science-centered curriculum. A school-based decision making council sought expertise for developing the outdoor lab from The Kentucky Department of Forestry, Soil and Conservation Department, and the Fish and Wildlife Service. K-4 teachers chose "Environment" as the main theme around which nine thematic units were developed. The units are the framework for a totally integrated program with science as the central unifying discipline. The instructional strategies are grounded in Howard Gardner's seven multiple intelligences. Learning is relevant to the real world and assessment is authentic.

Innovative Features: The science-centered interdisciplinary curriculum is the most innovative feature of the program. In addition, staff collaboration and parent and community involvement are essential innovations.

Goals: The primary goal of the **Hands-On Environment Program** is to help each child learn the skills, knowledge, and attitudes needed to be a responsible caretaker of the environment while linking education to the world and fostering a lifelong desire for learning.

Effectiveness: Teachers perceive that the needs of more students are being met without pullout programs and that students achieve more.

Staff Support: The program is to be implemented by K-4 primary teachers who will need orientation and staff development on techniques of collaboration and implementation of instructional strategies related to Gardner's seven multiple intelligences.

(Year initiated: 1991)

NCISE Standards met:

- ☑ Accessible to all students.
- ☑ Build on students' prior experience and knowledge.
- ☑ Use an instructional model based on the scientific process such as: question, discover, create, communicate, and pursue new questions.
- ☑ Relate to personal and social needs.
- ☑ Select science concepts that are developmentally appropriate, with illustrative examples drawn from the content of multiple disciplines of science.
- ☑ Develop scientific thinking skills such as drawing conclusions based on evidence, using inference, creating models.
- ☑ Develop scientific habits of mind such as curiosity, skepticism, honesty, living with ambiguity.
- ☑ Use authentic assessments to chart teaching and learning.
- ☑ Shift the role of teacher from imparter of knowledge to designer and facilitator of learning.
- ☑ Seek relevant and significant applications of science content and concepts to students' personal and community life.

NCTM standards met:

- ☑ Pose tasks based on sound and significant mathematics.
- ☑ Build on students' prior experience and knowledge.
- ☑ Develop mathematics thinking skills that convince students of the validity of particular representations, solutions, conjectures, and answers.
- ☑ Engage students' intellect; pose questions and tasks that elicit, engage, and challenge each students' thinking.
- ☑ Develop students' mathematical knowledge and skills.
- ☑ Stimulate students to make connections and develop a coherent framework for mathematical ideas.
- ☑ Call for problem formulation, problem solving, and mathematical reasoning.
- ☑ Promote the development of all students' dispositions to do mathematics.
- ☑ Develop an instructional model based on the range of ways students learn mathematics.

RESOURCES/MATERIALS NEEDED FOR ADOPTION:

The following resources/materials are needed for adoption: teacher-made supplies for the learning centers; supplemental instructional materials for the thematic units; Literature-based books for group reading; and source for experts related to the school's focus to share their knowledge

Equipment Needed:

- Manipulatives
- Acreage for an outdoor lab

Support Needed:

- Staff Orientation
- Consultants/Trainers
- Teacher Collaboration/Support Groups

Note: The following support services are considered necessary: professional expertise from the Kentucky Forestry Service, Soil Conservation Department, and the Fish and Wildlife Service along with the willingness of teachers to collaborate, cooperate, and share.

FUNDED BY: District and Business Grants

CONTACT:
Betty Fox, Teacher
Albert Benjamin Chandler Elementary
11215 U.S. Hwy. 60 W
Corydon, KY 42406
(Mail Inquiries Only)

SITE(S):
Albert Benjamin Chandler Elementary School
11215 U.S. Hwy 60 W
Corydon, KY 42406

Source: Appalachia Educational Laboratory

HAWAII MARINE SCIENCE STUDIES (HMSS)

University of Hawaii
Honolulu, HI

HMSS: A Marine-Based Science and Technology Program

TOPIC: Multidisciplinary, Environmental Studies, Physics, Earth/Space Science, Chemistry, Biology

USER(S): 9-12 educators

TARGET POPULATION: All Students

EMPHASIS ON:

Instructional Materials	Teaching Strategies	Assessment Tools
• Self-Contained Program/Packet	• Hands-On Learning	• Student Assessment Materials
• Teaching Lessons/Units	• Student-Centered Learning	• Teacher Reaction Inventories
• Technology-Based Materials	• Thematic Teaching Approach	• Technology-Based Tools
	• Cooperative/Group Learning	• Teacher Evaluations
	• Technology-Based Strategies	

GENERAL DESCRIPTION

The **HMSS** is a one-year multidisciplinary science course set in a marine context for students in grades 9-12. There are two companion student books in the program: THE FLUID EARTH and THE LIVING OCEAN. THE FLUID EARTH explores the physics, chemistry, and geology of the oceans and their applications in ocean engineering and related technologies. THE LIVING OCEAN explores the biology and ecology of the oceans and other aquatic environments and their application in aquaculture and related technologies.

Innovative Features: THE FLUID EARTH is the only physical marine science textbook for the high school available in the United States. The program allows students to build their own knowledge by involving approximately 70% of student learning time in environmental aspects of science and links their findings to the practical societal world.

Goals: The goals of marine education are to develop awareness, knowledge, and understanding of the ocean's relationship to the total environment and the ocean's particular influence on humankind and society. Of key importance is the development of a commitment to the wise use of the oceans and all other environments.

Effectiveness: In the fall of 1992 HMSS was in use by 20,000 students in Hawaii and on the mainland U.S.

Staff Support: A two-week teacher institute is required.

(Year initiated: 1982)

NCISE Standards met:

☑ Accessible to all students.

☑ Build on students' prior experience and knowledge.

☑ Use an instructional model based on the scientific process such as: question, discover, create, communicate, and pursue new questions.

☑ Relate to personal and social needs.

☑ Select science concepts that are developmentally appropriate, with illustrative examples drawn from the content of multiple disciplines of science.

☑ Develop scientific thinking skills such as drawing conclusions based on evidence, using inference, creating models.

☑ Develop scientific habits of mind such as curiosity, skepticism, honesty, living with ambiguity.

☑ Use authentic assessments to chart teaching and learning.

☑ Shift the role of teacher from imparter of knowledge to designer and facilitator of learning.

☑ Seek relevant and significant applications of science content and concepts to students' personal and community life.

NCTM standards met:

☐ Pose tasks based on sound and significant mathematics.

☐ Build on students' prior experience and knowledge.

☐ Develop mathematics thinking skills that convince students of the validity of particular representations, solutions, conjectures, and answers.

☐ Engage students' intellect; pose questions and tasks that elicit, engage, and challenge each students' thinking.

☐ Develop students' mathematical knowledge and skills.

☐ Stimulate students to make connections and develop a coherent framework for mathematical ideas.

☐ Call for problem formulation, problem solving, and mathematical reasoning.

☐ Promote the development of all students' dispositions to do mathematics.

☐ Develop an instructional model based on the range of ways students learn mathematics.

RESOURCES/MATERIALS NEEDED FOR ADOPTION:

Student Texts (2)

Equipment Needed:

• Software

• Videodisc Player

• Macintosh Computer

Support Needed:

• Training Packets

• Workshop/Inservice

• Consultants/Trainers

FUNDED BY: Sea Grant from the University of Hawaii

CONTACT:

Francis M. Pottenger, Professor
University of Hawaii
1776 University Avenue, UHS-204
Honolulu, HI 96822
(808) 956-6918
Fax: (808) 956-9486

SITE(S):

University Laboratory School
University of Hawaii
1776 University Ave
Honolulu, HI 96822
(808) 956-7833

Source: Pacific Region Educational Laboratory

THE HAYES COOPER CENTER FOR MATH, SCIENCE, AND TECHNOLOGY

The Hayes Center for Math, Science and Technology
Merigold, MS

An Elementary Magnet School with Special Emphasis on Math and Science

TOPIC: Elementary Math, General Math, Elementary Science, Environmental Studies, Biology/Life Science, Earth/Space Science

USER(S): K-6 Educators, Curriculum Specialists, School Administrators, Technology Specialists

TARGET POPULATION: At-Risk, Ethnic/Minority, Rural, Gifted

EMPHASIS ON:

Instructional Materials	Teaching Strategies	Assessment Tools
• N/A	• N/A	• N/A

GENERAL DESCRIPTION

The Hayes Cooper Center is an elementary magnet school in Merigold, Mississippi, with special emphasis on math and science.

Innovative Features: Every student learns to speak a foreign language and understand a different culture and, is computer literate. The students explore science by getting their hands dirty and observing the world just outside their classrooms. They experiment with ideas that they previously only read about in textbooks, and make mathematics a practical part of their everyday lives with understandable applications and hands-on manipulatives.

Goals: Goals expand upon the aim that every student will progress academically every day. The Center brings together students of different social, economic, racial, and ethnic backgrounds. It provides an educational setting that measures success in national and international terms rather than shooting for the state's mean. The Center seeks to eliminate minority isolation in the Cleveland community at the elementary school level by maintaining a 50/50 racial composition. Cultural diversity is celebrated as the individual's unique background, interests, goals, and desires are emphasized.

Effectiveness: The Center is a learning model lab for public schools across the Delta, the state, and region. It tutors 190 students with plans to more than double its size by Fall 1993. Attendance is by choice with enrollment selected randomly from formal district-wide applications.

(Year initiated: 1991)

NCISE Standards met:

☑ Accessible to all students.

☐ Build on students' prior experience and knowledge.

☐ Use an instructional model based on the scientific process such as: question, discover, create, communicate, and pursue new questions.

☐ Relate to personal and social needs.

☐ Select science concepts that are developmentally appropriate, with illustrative examples drawn from the content of multiple disciplines of science.

☐ Develop scientific thinking skills such as drawing conclusions based on evidence, using inference, creating models.

☑ Develop scientific habits of mind such as curiosity, skepticism, honesty, living with ambiguity.

☐ Use authentic assessments to chart teaching and learning.

☐ Shift the role of teacher from imparter of knowledge to designer and facilitator of learning.

☑ Seek to find relevant and significant applications of science content and concepts to students' personal and community life.

NCTM standards met:

☑ Pose tasks based on sound and significant mathematics.

☑ Build on students' prior experience and knowledge.

☑ Develop mathematics thinking skills that convince students of the validity of particular representations, solutions, conjectures, and answers.

☑ Engage students' intellect; pose questions and tasks that elicit, engage, and challenge each students' thinking.

☑ Develop students' mathematical knowledge and skills.

☑ Stimulate students to make connections and develop a coherent framework for mathematical ideas.

☑ Call for problem formulation, problem solving, and mathematical reasoning.

☑ Promote the development of all students' dispositions to do mathematics.

☐ Develop an instructional model based on the range of ways students learn mathematics.

RESOURCES/MATERIALS NEEDED FOR ADOPTION:

The computer emphasis at the Hayes Cooper Center requires a significant investment in hardware and software, including a file server to operate the network.

Equipment Needed:

• IBM Compatible Computer Equipment

• Special Hands-On Equipment

Support Needed:

• Staff Development

• Technical Assistance

• Workshop/Inservice

• Teacher Collaborations/Support Groups

Note: Extensive teacher training is crucial to implement this program which emphasizes alternative teaching methods, a reliance on computer instruction and hands-on science and math instruction. Technical advice in integrating computers into the curriculum was provided by computer companies, state department of education experts, and university professors.

FUNDED BY: Chapter 1, Chapter II, National Science Foundation, Eisenhower Mathematics and Science Education Program, District, State

CONTACT:

SERVE Consortium for Mathematics and Science Education
345 S. Magnolia Dr., Suite D-23
Tallahassee, FL 32301-2950
(904) 922-8533; (800) 854-0476
Fax: (904) 922-8068

SITE(S):

The Hayes Cooper Center for Math, Science and Technology
Route 1 Box 3, Highway 61 North
Merigold, MS 38759

Source: SouthEastern Regional Vision for Education

THE INSTITUTE FOR SCIENCE AND MATHEMATICS (ISM)

Grant High School
Portland, OR

Increasing Student Awareness of Science & Mathematics Through Experiential Learning

TOPIC: General Math, Pre-Algebra, Algebra I, Geometry, Algebra II, Trigonometry, Calculus, Technology Studies, Environmental Studies, Biology/Life Science, Physics, Earth/Space Science, Chemistry

USER(S): 9-12 Educators, Curriculum Specialists, School Administrators, Technology Specialists, Parents, Researchers, Paraprofessionals

TARGET POPULATION: Urban, At-Risk, Ethnic/Minority, Honors/Advanced Placement, Learning Disabilities, Female

EMPHASIS ON:

Instructional Materials

- Supplemental Learning/Teaching Materials
- Thematic Instructional Package
- Teaching Package with Lessons/Units
- Curriculum Guides
- Technology-Based Materials

Teaching Strategies

- Hands-On Learning
- Student-Centered Learning
- Thematic Teaching Approach
- Cooperative/Group Learning
- Technology-Based Strategies

Assessment Tools

- Student Assessment Materials
- Attitude Surveys/Inventories
- Program Review Materials
- Needs Assessment Surveys
- Portfolios
- Technology-Based Tools

GENERAL DESCRIPTION

The **ISM** challenges students through a continuous-study core curriculum. ISM students enroll in an introductory common course which also functions as an advisory class in the transition to high school.

Innovative Features: The ISM successfully combines several emerging curriculum projects and research-based practices into a specialized high school experience accessible to all students. The ISM expands the content of secondary mathematics and science to include areas such as statistical data analysis, probability, discrete mathematics, spatial reasoning, real world science, and ethics. It uses technology, graphing calculators and computers and includes self-assessment, student portfolios, teacher observations, and group work.

Goals: The goals of the ISM are to excite student interest in mathematics and science; to increase minority and female student enrollment in mathematics and science courses; and to develop students' potential to meet the changing demands of higher education, business, and industry.

Effectiveness: Enrollment in mathematics and science classes has increased between eight and twelve percent and is more representative of the neighborhood ratio of students by gender, ethnicity, and achievement levels. Last year, failure rate for Interactive Mathematics was three percent compared to 25% in regular first-year Algebra classes. Student portfolios document extensive participation in co-curricular math and science activities. Staff, students, and parents report increased student confidence and broader knowledge of mathematics and science.

Staff Support: The program is implemented by high school educators with the support of curriculum specialists, school administrators, technology specialists, parents, and paraprofessionals.

(Year initiated: 1989)

NCISE Standards met:

☑ Accessible to all students.

☑ Build on students' prior experience and knowledge.

☑ Use an instructional model based on the scientific process such as: question, discover, create, communicate, and pursue new questions.

☑ Relate to personal and social needs.

☑ Select science concepts that are developmentally appropriate, with illustrative examples drawn from the content of multiple disciplines of science.

☑ Develop scientific thinking skills such as drawing conclusions based on evidence, using inference, creating models.

☑ Develop scientific habits of mind such as curiosity, skepticism, honesty, living with ambiguity.

☑ Use authentic assessments to chart teaching and learning.

☑ Shift the role of teacher from imparter of knowledge to designer and facilitator of learning.

☑ Seek relevant and significant applications of science content and concepts to students' personal and community life.

NCTM standards met:

☑ Pose tasks based on sound and significant mathematics.

☑ Build on students' prior experience and knowledge.

☑ Develop mathematics thinking skills that convince students of the validity of particular representations, solutions, conjectures, and answers.

☑ Engage students' intellect; pose questions and tasks that elicit, engage, and challenge each students' thinking.

☑ Develop students' mathematical knowledge and skills.

☑ Stimulate students to make connections and develop a coherent framework for mathematical ideas.

☑ Call for problem formulation, problem solving, and mathematical reasoning.

☑ Promote the development of all students' dispositions to do mathematics.

☑ Develop an instructional model based on the range of ways students learn mathematics.

RESOURCES/MATERIALS NEEDED FOR ADOPTION:

The ISM classes use a combination of adapted classroom-tested materials and teacher-developed lessons. The Interactive Mathematics Project curriculum units are the basis of the three-year Interactive Mathematics course which replaces the traditional courses. Salters' Science, developed at the University of York, England, is similarly replacing more conventional text-based science study throughout the department. These materials require few additional resources although manipulative math materials and class sets of graphing calculators are needed.

Equipment Needed:

- Manipulatives
- Graphing calculators

Support Needed:

- Implementation of significant changes in both content and instructional methods requires an array of support, including orientation, staff development, technical assistance, workshop/inservice, consultants/trainers, teacher collaborations, and support groups.

- Most effective are monthly collaborative planning meetings and approximately thirty hours of inservice activities yearly for mathematics and science teachers. In addition the "ISM Roundtable" combines collegial support with action-research projects.

FUNDED BY: State Eisenhower grant, District. National Science Foundation funded the work of the Interactive Mathematics Project in California. No National Science Foundation funds directly support the ISM.

CONTACT:
Fred Rectanus, Program Coordinator
Grant High School
2245 N. E. 36th Avenue
Portland, OR 97212
(Mail Inquiries Only)

SITE(S):
Grant High School
2245 N. E. 36th Avenue
Portland, OR 97212

Source: Northwest Regional Educational Laboratory

JIMMY HUNTINGTON SCHOOL CARIBOU/FISHERIES PROJECT

Jimmy Huntington School
Huslia, AK

Culturally Significant K-12 Integrated Science Project

TOPIC: Elementary Math, Multidisciplinary Studies, General Math, Pre-Algebra, Algebra I, Algebra II, Elementary Science, Environmental Studies, Biology/Life Science

USER(S): K-12 Educators, School Administrators, Parents

TARGET POPULATION: Rural, Ethnic/Minority

EMPHASIS ON:

Instructional Materials	Teaching Strategies	Assessment Tools
• N/A	• Hands-On Learning	• N/A
	• Student-Centered Learning	
	• Thematic Teaching Approach	
	• Whole Language Approach	
	• Cooperative/Group Learning	
	• Individualized/Self-Paced Learning	
	• Technology-Based Strategies	

GENERAL DESCRIPTION

The **Jimmy Huntington School Caribou/Fisheries Project** provides a hands-on, culturally relevant science experience for students in grades K-12. The project is based on the philosophy that science should be taught every day through integration, should draw on the local environment, and should be culturally relevant.

Innovative Features: The students generate course content while the teachers serve as facilitators. Most of the resources and expertise come directly from the local community and surrounding area with other outside agencies as partners in the experience. The integration of science, mathematics, and language arts is a fundamental part of the project.

Goals: The project has three goals: to increase the amount of time students are exposed to science, to integrate science with the rest of the curriculum, and to utilize local resources and persons.

Effectiveness: The project has resulted in a marked improvement of basic science skills for entering junior high students. An increase in parental involvement in science projects and lessons has also been noted.

Staff Support: The project is implemented by K-12 teachers who need to be provided with time for staff collaboration and planning.

(Year initiated: 1991)

NCISE Standards met:

☑ Accessible to all students.

☑ Build on students' prior experience and knowledge.

☑ Use an instructional model based on the scientific process such as: question, discover, create, communicate, and pursue new questions.

☑ Relate to personal and social needs.

☑ Select science concepts that are developmentally appropriate, with illustrative examples drawn from the content of multiple disciplines of science.

☑ Develop scientific thinking skills such as drawing conclusions based on evidence, using inference, creating models.

☑ Develop scientific habits of mind such as curiosity, skepticism, honesty, living with ambiguity.

☑ Use authentic assessments to chart teaching and learning.

☑ Shift the role of teacher from imparter of knowledge to designer and facilitator of learning.

☑ Seek relevant and significant applications of science content and concepts to students' personal and community life.

NCTM standards met:

☑ Pose tasks based on sound and significant mathematics.

☑ Build on students' prior experience and knowledge.

☐ Develop mathematics thinking skills that convince students of the validity of particular representations, solutions, conjectures, and answers.

☑ Engage students' intellect; pose questions and tasks that elicit, engage, and challenge each students' thinking.

☑ Develop students' mathematical knowledge and skills.

☑ Stimulate students to make connections and develop a coherent framework for mathematical ideas.

☑ Call for problem formulation, problem solving, and mathematical reasoning.

☑ Promote the development of all students' dispositions to do mathematics.

☐ Develop an instructional model based on the range of ways students learn mathematics.

RESOURCES/MATERIALS NEEDED FOR ADOPTION:

Local materials, resources and expertise, district curriculum guides, and appropriate materials from outside agencies are necessary resources for this approach.

Equipment Needed:

• N/A

Support Needed:

• Technical Assistance

• Workshop/Inservice

• Consultants/Trainers

• Teacher Collaboration/Support Groups

Note: We have called on Alaska Fish and Game and U.S. Fish and Wildlife personnel to provide information and demonstrations where possible. For the second year of the project, an inservice is necessary to organize and develop the annual goals and objectives. One staff member serves as the specialist to oversee the program and provide assistance. Updates are provided at regular staff meetings.

FUNDED BY: District

CONTACT:
Michele B. Bifelt
Teacher
P.O. Box 69
Huslia, AK 99746
(Mail Inquiries Only)

SITE:
Jimmy Huntington School
P. O. Box 110
Huslia, AK 99746

Source: Northwest Regional Educational Laboratory

MATHEMATICS, ENGINEERING, SCIENCE ACHIEVEMENT (MESA)

University of Colorado at Denver, College of Engineering
Denver, CO

Pre-college Support for Minority Students Interested in Pursuing Careers in Science, Engineering and Math Related Areas

TOPIC: Multidisciplinary Studies

USER(S): 6-12 Educators

TARGET POPULATION: Ethnic/Minority

EMPHASIS ON:

Instructional Materials	Teaching Strategies	Assessment Tools
• Technology-Based Materials	• Technology-Based Strategies	• N/A
	• Mentoring	
	• Student-Centered Learning	

GENERAL DESCRIPTION

The **CMEA/MESA** program encourages promising young minority students to focus on their futures as early as sixth grade and to consider future careers in engineering and science. It stimulates career awareness and motivation through field trips, role model speakers, competitions, incentive awards, college and career counseling, summer enrichment opportunities, and internships.

Innovative Features: CMEA/MESA includes significant connections with professional engineering societies, business, industry and academia. It involves parents in the educational and motivational process, and an Incentive Award Program provides students with the opportunity to earn valuable rewards for their academic achievement and participation. The program also involves a peer group that encourages interest and achievement in the science and math fields.

Goals: CMEA/MESA develops interest in science, engineering, and related fields. Its goal is to graduate students who are ready to enter universities fully prepared to succeed in an engineering or science major.

Effectiveness: The effectiveness of the CMEA/MESA program is measured primarily by how many students go on to college. MESA seniors, three-fourths of whom are minority, have matriculated at rates of 96%, 95%, and 97% in the last three years.

Staff Support: The key component is the school's CMEA/MESA advisor who monitors students' progress and makes sure they remain on a college prep track. Incentives such as scientific calculators and computers motivate and support student interest and participation.

(Year initiated: 1980)

NCISE Standards met:

☑ Accessible to all students.

☐ Build on students' prior experience and knowledge.

☐ Use an instructional model based on the scientific process such as: question, discover, create, communicate, and pursue new questions.

☐ Relate to personal and social needs.

☐ Select science concepts that are developmentally appropriate, with illustrative examples drawn from the content of multiple disciplines of science.

☐ Develop scientific thinking skills such as drawing conclusions based on evidence, using inference, creating models.

☐ Develop scientific habits of mind such as curiosity, skepticism, honesty, living with ambiguity.

☐ Use authentic assessments to chart teaching and learning.

☐ Shift the role of teacher from imparter of knowledge to designer and facilitator of learning.

☐ Seek relevant and significant applications of science content and concepts to students' personal and community life.

NCTM standards met:

☐ Pose tasks based on sound and significant mathematics.

☐ Build on students' prior experience and knowledge.

☐ Develop mathematics thinking skills that convince students of the validity of particular representations, solutions, conjectures, and answers.

☐ Engage students' intellect; pose questions and tasks that elicit, engage, and challenge each students' thinking.

☐ Develop students' mathematical knowledge and skills.

☐ Stimulate students to make connections and develop a coherent framework for mathematical ideas.

☐ Call for problem formulation, problem solving, and mathematical reasoning.

☑ Promote the development of all students' dispositions to do mathematics.

☐ Develop an instructional model based on the range of ways students learn mathematics.

RESOURCES/MATERIALS NEEDED FOR ADOPTION:

This program makes maximum use of existing resources in the school, including staff and course offerings. The key component is the school's CMEA/MESA advisor who monitors students' progress and makes sure they remain on a college prep track. Materials that support and motivate student interest and participation include incentives such as scientific calculators and computers.

Equipment Needed: (if technology focused)

- Computer Equipment
  (IBM compatible, Apple Macintosh)
- Modem
- Software

Support Needed:

- Orientation
- Videotapes
- Workshop/Inservice
- Consultant/Trainers
- Teacher Collaboration/Support Groups

FUNDED BY: Corporate and Business Grants

CONTACT:

John Rael, Jr.
Executive Director, Colorado Minority
Engineering Assoc. (CMEA)
University of Colorado
College of Engineering
Campus Box 104, P.O. Box 173364
Denver, CO 80217-3364
(303) 556-2344

SITE(S):

Kepner Middle School
911 S. Hazel Ct.
Denver, CO 80219

(92 sites currently use this program)

Source: Mid-continent Regional Educational Laboratory

NEW HAMPSHIRE YOUNG INVENTORS' PROGRAM (NHYIP)

Academy of Applied Science
Concord, NH

Students Use Invention and Problem Solving to Develop Critical Thinking Skills

TOPIC: Elementary Math, General Math, Geometry, Elementary Science, Environmental Studies, Biology/Life Science, Physics, Earth/Space Science

USER(S): 1-8 Educators, Curriculum Specialists, School Administrators, Parents

TARGET POPULATION: Urban, At-Risk, Suburban, Ethnic/Minority, Rural, Gifted, Honors/Advanced, Placement, Learning Disabilities, Emotionally Handicapped, Female, Male

EMPHASIS ON:

Instructional Materials	Teaching Strategies	Assessment Tools
• Self-Contained Program/Packet	• Hands-On Learning	• N/A
• Supplemental Learning/Teaching Materials	• Student-Centered Learning	
• Teaching Lessons/Units	• Thematic Teaching Approach	
	• Individualized/Self-Paced Learning	

GENERAL DESCRIPTION

New Hampshire Young Inventors' Program (NHYIP) helps students develop critical thinking and problem-solving skills by challenging them to invent solutions to everyday problems. A major component of this project is local and statewide Invention Conventions where students display their projects, meet other student and adult inventors, and receive recognition for their accomplishments. (There are even workshops for parents.)

Innovative Features: The program was planned collaboratively by a consortium of teachers from New Hampshire school districts and the Academy of Applied Science. The invention process as well as the use of creative thinking and problem-solving represent innovative ways of learning.

Goals: The NHYIP aims to develop student problem-solving capabilities and creativity by defining a real problem, formulating an original solution, developing a product, and sharing the results or products with appropriate audiences.

Effectiveness: The first year of the program 82 student inventors attended the state Invention Convention from 21 schools. In 1992, 231 students attended from 55 schools. The program has grown to include over 5,000 students participating at the local level each year.

Staff Support: The Consortium members traveled around the state to promote the concept through teacher workshops and inservice trainings. The program has held two major teacher workshops with over 120 teachers participating. Evaluations completed by workshop and Invention Convention participants indicate continued enthusiasm.

(Year initiated: 1987)

NCISE Standards met:

☑ Accessible to all students.

☑ Build on students' prior experience and knowledge.

☑ Use an instructional model based on the scientific process such as: question, discover, create, communicate, and pursue new questions.

☑ Relate to personal and social needs.

☑ Select science concepts that are developmentally appropriate, with illustrative examples drawn from the content of multiple disciplines of science.

☑ Develop scientific thinking skills such as drawing conclusions based on evidence, using inference, creating models.

☑ Develop scientific habits of mind such as curiosity, skepticism, honesty, living with ambiguity.

☑ Use authentic assessments to chart teaching and learning.

☑ Shift the role of teacher from imparter of knowledge to designer and facilitator of learning.

☑ Seek relevant and significant applications of science content and concepts to students' personal and community life.

NCTM standards met:

☑ Pose tasks based on sound and significant mathematics.

☑ Build on students' prior experience and knowledge.

☑ Develop mathematics thinking skills that convince students of the validity of particular representations, solutions, conjectures, and answers.

☑ Engage students' intellect; pose questions and tasks that elicit, engage, and challenge each students' thinking.

☑ Develop students' mathematical knowledge and skills.

☑ Stimulate students to make connections and develop a coherent framework for mathematical ideas.

☑ Call for problem formulation, problem solving, and mathematical reasoning.

☐ Promote the development of all students' dispositions to do mathematics.

☐ Develop an instructional model based on the range of ways students learn mathematics.

RESOURCES/MATERIALS NEEDED FOR ADOPTION:

The New Hampshire Young Inventors' Program Teacher's Manual is a helpful resource. This manual is being updated for national distribution.

Equipment Needed:

• Varies with invention/solution

Support Needed:

• Staff Development

• Training Packets

• Workshop/Inservice

• Teacher Collaboration/Support Groups

Note: Teachers should be familiar with how to incorporate the invention program into their schools, as well as with techniques that inspire imaginative thinking and critical and creative problem solving in their classrooms.

FUNDED BY: Eisenhower Mathematics and Science Education Program, Academy of Applied Science, Area Businesses

CONTACT:

Susan W. Zehnder, Director
Academy of Applied Science
98 Washington Street
Concord, NH 03301
(603) 228-4530
Fax: (603) 228-4730/(603) 228-4730

SITE(S):

Boscawen Elementary School
Main Street
Boscawen, NH 03303

Source: The Regional Laboratory for Educational Improvement of the Northeast and the Islands

NORTH CAROLINA PROJECT FOR REFORM IN SCIENCE EDUCATION

East Carolina University
Greenville, NC

A Multidisciplinary Middle School Science Program

TOPIC: Multidisciplinary, Elementary/Middle School Science, General Math, Geometry

USER(S): 6-8 Educators

TARGET POPULATION: Urban, Suburban, Rural

EMPHASIS ON:

Instructional Materials

- Thematic Instructional Package
- Supplemental Learning/Teaching Materials
- Teaching Package with Lessons/Units
- Curriculum Guides

Teaching Strategies

- Hands-On Learning
- Student-Centered Learning
- Thematic Teaching Approach
- Cooperative/Group Learning
- Technology-Based Strategies

Assessment Tools

- Student Performance Assessment Materials
- Attitude Surveys/Inventories
- Teacher Reaction Inventories
- Program Review Materials
- Needs Assessment Surveys
- Portfolios

GENERAL DESCRIPTION

The **North Carolina Project for Reform in Science Education** (NCPRSE) is part of a nationwide initiative to provide meaningful science experiences to every student in grades 6-8 in biology, chemistry, earth, and physical sciences. Students initially encounter science concepts, principles, and laws at a concrete level through direct experiences with phenomenon. Later, students interact with science at successively higher levels of abstraction.

Innovative Features: The curriculum is produced by the teachers and tested in the classroom. Strategies are research-based and the content framework is a synthesis of the most current recommendations from scientists and national organizations.

Goals: The program is based on the axiom that "all children can learn." The teachers must redefine their role as imparters of knowledge and assume roles as facilitators, questioning and guiding each child.

Effectiveness: Effectiveness is determined by evaluations on performance-based items that target content and process acquisition.

(Year initiated: 1989)

NCISE Standards met:

☑ Accessible to all students.

☑ Build on students' prior experience and knowledge.

☑ Use an instructional model based on the scientific process such as: question, discover, create, communicate, and pursue new questions.

☑ Relate to personal and social needs.

☑ Select science concepts that are developmentally appropriate, with illustrative examples drawn from the content of multiple disciplines of science.

☑ Develop scientific thinking skills such as drawing conclusions based on evidence, using inference, creating models.

☑ Develop scientific habits of mind such as curiosity, skepticism, honesty, living with ambiguity.

☑ Use authentic assessments to chart teaching and learning.

☑ Shift the role of teacher from imparter of knowledge to designer and facilitator of learning.

☑ Seek to find relevant and significant applications of science content and concepts to students' personal and community life.

NCTM standards met:

☑ Pose tasks based on sound and significant mathematics.

☑ Build on students' prior experience and knowledge.

☑ Develop mathematics thinking skills that convince students of the validity of particular representations, solutions, conjectures, and answers.

☑ Engage students' intellect; pose questions and tasks that elicit, engage, and challenge each students' thinking.

☑ Develop students' mathematical knowledge and skills.

☑ Stimulate students to make connections and develop a coherent framework for mathematical ideas.

☑ Call for problem formulation, problem solving, and mathematical reasoning.

☑ Promote the development of all students' dispositions to do mathematics.

☑ Develop an instructional model based on the range of ways students learn mathematics.

RESOURCES/MATERIALS NEEDED FOR ADOPTION:

Curriculum and staff development are critical components for the adoption of the program. Activities for family involvement also are encouraged.

Equipment Needed:

• Special Hands-On Equipment

• Manipulatives

• Teachers Manual

• Other Optional Equipment

Support Needed:

• Orientation

• Workshop/Inservice

• Consultants/Trainers

• Training Tapes

• Technical Assistance

• Teacher Collaborations

FUNDED BY: National Science Foundation, Eisenhower Mathematics and Science Education Program

CONTACT:

SERVE Consortium for Mathematics
and Science Education
345 S. Magnolia Dr., Suite D-23
Tallahassee, FL 32301-2950
(904) 922-8533; (800) 854-0476
Fax: (904) 922-8068

SITE(S):

Valley Springs Middle School, Arden, NC
A.G. Cox Middle School, Winterville, NC
Hanes Middle School, Winston Salem, NC

Source: SouthEastern Regional Vision for Education

PROGRAM ASSESSMENT: AN APPROACH FOR IMPROVING INSTRUCTION IN SCIENCE: A WORKING MODEL

Bristol Elementary School
Bristol, VT

Performance-Based Activities Measure Curriculum and Instructional Effectiveness Against New Standards

TOPIC: Elementary Math, Elementary Science

USER(S): K-9 Educators, Curriculum Specialists, School Administrators, Program Planners

TARGET POPULATION: All Students

EMPHASIS ON:

Instructional Materials	Teaching Strategies	Assessment Tools
• N/A	• N/A	• Student Assessment Materials,
		• Attitude Surveys/Inventories,
		• Teacher Reaction Inventories,
		• Program Review Materials
		• Needs Assessment Surveys,
		• Portfolios

GENERAL DESCRIPTION

The **ANESU Math and Science Assessment Program** was developed by a committee of teachers, administrators, and curriculum specialists to measure the effectiveness of curriculum and instruction in meeting NCTM and NCISE standards.

The program features performance-based assessment activities, and a program assessment component based on student performance and teaching practices. It also includes a cyclical time line providing ongoing, continual program evaluation in math and science, and many locally developed assessment instruments such as surveys and instructional portfolios. Assessment activities are carried out by staff and faculty members with input received from students, faculty, parents, and community members.

Goals: The primary goal is to increase the quantity and improve the quality of student learning and growth in the district schools. Additional objectives are to assess educational inputs, implementation, and outputs; to be positive, engaging, and compatible with teaching and learning activities, and to provide useful information to teachers in an ongoing formative and summative manner.

Effectiveness: Ongoing assessment activities are evaluated annually with findings conveyed throughout the district. At the end of each four-year cycle recommendations are made concerning adjustments in the curriculum and teaching practices.

Staff Support: Program evaluations yield an action plan to guide educators in making curriculum and instructional changes.

(Year initiated: 1987)

NCISE Standards met:

☑ Accessible to all students.

☑ Build on students' prior experience and knowledge.

☑ Use an instructional model based on the scientific process such as: question, discover, create, communicate, and pursue new questions.

☑ Relate to personal and social needs.

☑ Select science concepts that are developmentally appropriate, with illustrative examples drawn from the content of multiple disciplines of science.

☑ Develop scientific thinking skills such as drawing conclusions based on evidence, using inference, creating models.

☑ Develop scientific habits of mind such as curiosity, skepticism, honesty, living with ambiguity.

☑ Use authentic assessments to chart teaching and learning.

☑ Shift the role of teacher from imparter of knowledge to designer and facilitator of learning.

☑ Seek relevant and significant applications of science content and concepts to students' personal and community life.

NCTM standards met:

☐ Pose tasks based on sound and significant mathematics.

☐ Build on students' prior experience and knowledge.

☐ Develop mathematics thinking skills that convince students of the validity of particular representations, solutions, conjectures, and answers.

☐ Engage students' intellect; pose questions and tasks that elicit, engage, and challenge each students' thinking.

☐ Develop students' mathematical knowledge and skills.

☐ Stimulate students to make connections and develop a coherent framework for mathematical ideas.

☐ Call for problem formulation, problem solving, and mathematical reasoning.

☐ Promote the development of all students' dispositions to do mathematics.

☐ Develop an instructional model based on the range of ways students learn mathematics.

RESOURCES/MATERIALS NEEDED FOR ADOPTION:

NY State Program Evaluation in Science Test with appropriate hands-on test materials (special permission required from NY State Dept. of Ed.).

Copies of Program Assessment Plans, surveys, and other assessment instruments from ANESU.

ANESU curriculum guidelines in math and science for reference.

Equipment Needed:

- Special Hands-On Equipment
- Manipulatives

Support Needed:

- Orientation
- Staff Development
- Technical Assistance
- Training Packets
- Workshop/Inservice
- Consultant/Trainers
- Teacher Collaboration/Support Groups

FUNDED BY: Chapter II, Eisenhower Mathematics and Science Education Program, District

CONTACT:
Pedie O'Brien or Neal Donahue
Assessment Committee Member
Bristol Elementary School
57 Mountain Street
Bristol, VT 05443
(Mail Inquiries Only)

SITE(S):
Bristol Elementary School
57 Mountain Street
Bristol, VT 05443

Source: The Regional Laboratory for Educational Improvement of the Northeast and the Islands

PROJECT PEAK

Mobile, AL

Magnet Schools for Math and Science

TOPIC: Multidisciplinary, General Math, Pre-Algebra, Environmental Studies, Biology/Life Science, Earth/Space Science, Physical Sciences

USER(S): K-8 Educators

TARGET POPULATION: Ethnic/Minority Students

EMPHASIS ON:

Instructional Materials

- N/A

Teaching Strategies

- Hands-On Learning
- Student-Centered Learning
- Whole-Language Approach
- Cooperative/Group Learning
- Technology-Based Strategies

Assessment Tools

- N/A

GENERAL DESCRIPTION

The Chickasaw and Clark Schools of Mathematics and Science established one elementary magnet and one middle magnet school during the 1991-1992 school year. The purposes of the program are to eliminate, reduce, or prevent the isolation of minority students and to provide students with courses of instruction that will reflect new math and science standards.

Innovative Features: This program uses computer-assisted instruction and mathematics and science manipulative labs. In addition, teachers enhance instruction by utilizing Talents Unlimited, Cooperative Learning, PEAK and other mini courses.

Goals: The goals of the program are to document the improvement of the student's self esteem, competency level in labs, and classroom and computer academic performance; to increase the student's interest in math and science related fields; and to provide an integrated atmosphere of acceptance and mutual respect for one another.

Effectiveness: The program is monitored and assessed by the individual school's staff, Mobile County Public School System supervisors, parent/community committees, the project facilitator, and the use of valid assessment instruments.

Staff Support: Extensive teacher training and staff development are an integral part of this program.

(Year initiated: 1991)

NCISE Standards met:

☑ Accessible to all students.

☑ Build on students' prior experience and knowledge.

☑ Use an instructional model based on the scientific process such as: question, discover, create, communicate, and pursue new questions.

☑ Relate to personal and social needs.

☑ Select science concepts that are developmentally appropriate, with illustrative examples drawn from the content of multiple disciplines of science.

☑ Develop scientific thinking skills such as drawing conclusions based on evidence, using inference, creating models.

☑ Develop scientific habits of mind such as curiosity, skepticism, honesty, living with ambiguity.

☑ Use authentic assessments to chart teaching and learning.

☑ Shift the role of teacher from imparter of knowledge to designer and facilitator of learning.

☑ Seek relevant and significant applications of science content and concepts to students' personal and community life.

NCTM standards met:

☑ Pose tasks based on sound and significant mathematics.

☑ Build on students' prior experience and knowledge.

☑ Develop mathematics thinking skills that convince students of the validity of particular representations, solutions, conjectures, and answers.

☑ Engage students' intellect; pose questions and tasks that elicit, engage, and challenge each students' thinking.

☑ Develop students' mathematical knowledge and skills.

☑ Stimulate students to make connections and develop a coherent framework for mathematical ideas.

☑ Call for problem formulation, problem solving, and mathematical reasoning.

☑ Promote the development of all students' dispositions to do mathematics.

☑ Develop an instructional model based on the range of ways students learn mathematics.

RESOURCES/MATERIALS NEEDED FOR ADOPTION:

Video disc programs, computer hardware and software, and lab manipulatives that support the math/science theme are important program tools.

Equipment Needed:

• VCR and Monitor

• Manipulatives

• IBM or Macintosh Computer

• Software

• Videodisc Player

• Hands-On Equipment

Support Needed:

• Orientation

• Staff Development

• Technical Assistance

• Training Packets

• Workshop/Inservice

• Consultants/Trainers

• Teacher Collaboration/Support Groups

• Computers and Software

FUNDED BY: Federal Grant

CONTACT:

SERVE Consortium for Mathematics
and Science Education
345 S. Magnolia Dr., Suite D-23
Tallahassee, FL 32301-2950
(904) 922-8533; (800) 854-0476
Fax: (904) 922-8068

SITE(S):

Chickasaw School of Mathematics & Science
201 N. Craft Hwy.
Chickasaw, AL 36611

Clark School of Mathematics & Science
1712 Hand Ave.
Mobile, AL 36612

Source: SouthEastern Regional Vision for Education

PROJECT SMART
(SCIENCE AND MATHEMATICS FOR ARIZONA'S RURAL TEACHERS)

San Manuel, AZ

Rural Teacher Consortia for Leadership and Staff Development as well as Technical Assistance

TOPIC: Elementary Math, Elementary Science, Environmental Studies, Biology/Life Science Earth/Space Science, Chemistry, Physics

USER(S): K-8 Educators, Curriculum Specialists, School Administrators

TARGET POPULATION: Rural, At-Risk, Ethnic/Minority

EMPHASIS ON:

Instructional Materials	Teaching Strategies	Assessment Tools
• Supplemental Learning/Teaching Materials	• Hands-On Learning	• Student Performance
• Teaching Lessons/Units	• Student-Centered Learning	• Assessment Materials
• Curriculum Guides	• Thematic Teaching Approach	• Attitude Surveys/Inventories
• Technology-Based Materials	• Whole Language Teaching Approach	• Teacher Reaction Inventories
	• Cooperative/Group Learning	• Needs Assessment Surveys
	• Technology-Based Strategies	• Portfolios
		• Technology-Based Tools

GENERAL DESCRIPTION

Project SMART is a model for rural regional training and resource centers to support change and improvement in small schools. It has been instrumental in leveraging state Eisenhower funds to be allocated to seven other rural regional training centers for several consortia of rural districts.

Innovative Features: By combining districts' Eisenhower moneys and having a teacher-leader in each regional consortia, each district gets significant staff development, which brings all the components of excellent science education to teachers — hands-on strategies, cutting-edge curriculum materials, constructivist teaching, cooperative learning, alternative assessments, technology use.

Goals: The primary goal is to help teachers and administrators to develop the understandings, positive attitudes, and abilities to teach good mathematics and science. Project SMART also seeks to gather and disseminate information on rural staff development, instructional support, curriculum implementation, and partnerships, and to establish a working network of administrators and teachers from rural areas focused on science and math improvement.

Effectiveness: Teacher-leaders from Project SMART are actively involved in five of the regional training centers. Inservice courses developed by the project have Northern Arizona Early evaluative results indicate changes and gains in teacher attitudes, content, amount of time spent teaching science, and use of teaching strategies.

Staff Support: A cadre of teacher-leaders is trained over 3 summers in what is good K-8 science and mathematics education. They develop workshops which they conduct across states in each others' districts and regions. In addition there are one week institutes for regular classroom teachers.

(Year initiated: 1991)

NCISE Standards met:

☑ Accessible to all students.

☑ Build on students' prior experience and knowledge.

☑ Use an instructional model based on the scientific process such as: question, discover, create, communicate, and pursue new questions.

☑ Relate to personal and social needs.

☑ Select science concepts that are developmentally appropriate, with illustrative examples drawn from the content of multiple disciplines of science.

☑ Develop scientific thinking skills such as drawing conclusions based on evidence, using inference, creating models.

☑ Develop scientific habits of mind such as curiosity, skepticism, honesty, living with ambiguity.

☑ Use authentic assessments to chart teaching and learning.

☑ Shift the role of teacher from imparter of knowledge to designer and facilitator of learning.

☑ Seek relevant and significant applications of science content and concepts to students' personal and community life.

NCTM standards met:

☑ Pose tasks based on sound and significant mathematics.

☑ Build on students' prior experience and knowledge.

☑ Develop mathematics thinking skills that convince students of the validity of particular representations, solutions, conjectures, and answers.

☑ Engage students' intellect; pose questions and tasks that elicit, engage, and challenge each students' thinking.

☑ Develop students' mathematical knowledge and skills.

☑ Stimulate students to make connections and develop a coherent framework for mathematical ideas.

☑ Call for problem formulation, problem solving, and mathematical reasoning.

☑ Promote the development of all students' dispositions to do mathematics.

☑ Develop an instructional model based on the range of ways students learn mathematics.

RESOURCES/MATERIALS NEEDED FOR ADOPTION:

No specific materials are needed, but a variety of nationally recognized materials that support exemplary science and math are required. Those used currently include BSCS "Science for Life and Living," Family Math, and Family Science, among others.

Equipment Needed:

• Manipulatives

Support Needed:

• Staff Development

• Technical Assistance

• Training Packets

• Workshop/Inservice

• Consultants/Trainers

Note: Training requires more than one week. There are 2-week institutes over 3 consecutive summers for teacher leaders, and 1-week institutes for teachers (6 total).

FUNDED BY: Eisenhower Mathematics and Science Education Program, Arizona Community Foundation, National Science Foundation

CONTACT:
Brownie Sternberg
Project Director
700 McNab Parkway
San Manuel, AZ 85631
(Mail Inquiries Only)

SITE(S):
Other Regional Training Centers in Arizona have linkages to Project SMART.

Source: Far West Laboratory

SANDPIPER IN SPACE

Sandpiper Elementary School
Scottsdale, AZ

K-6 Multi-Disciplinary Science and Math Program Focused On Space Science

TOPIC: Elementary Math, General Math, Elementary Science, Environmental Studies, Earth/Space Science

USER(S): K-6 Educators, Curriculum Specialists, School Administrators, State Policy Makers, Paraprofessionals, Media Specialists, Parents

TARGET POPULATION: All Students

EMPHASIS ON:

Instructional Materials	Teaching Strategies	Assessment Tools
• Teaching Lessons/Units	• Hands-On Learning	• N/A
• Curriculum Guides	• Thematic Teaching Approach	
• Technology-Based Materials	• Cooperative/Group Learning	
	• Technology-Based Strategies	

GENERAL DESCRIPTION

In **Sandpiper in Space**, students "experience" life in space by participating in space-related activities in a mock 26-foot space shuttle.

Innovative Features: The space shuttle and a science lab allow students to "see" science even before they participate in it. Students are introduced to the shuttle in kindergarten when they visit the shuttle, sit in the cockpit, lab, and living quarters and talk about space.

Goals: The goals are: (1) to stimulate and motivate students' interest in science and (2) to teach and reinforce higher-order thinking. In-school activities are supplemented by major field trips, such as Space Camp, and by encouraging students to join out-of-school activities such as after-school Young Astronauts and summer activities for individual students. Computer-assisted simulations of space flights challenge students to work together to make decisions and pursue scientific investigation.

Effectiveness: Students show a high interest in science in school, both in class and in after-school enrichment classes. Sandpiper has been recognized as an exemplary site for science education throughout the U.S. The feeder high school has added an Aerospace Signature Program as a direct result of the Sandpiper Space Program. Sandpiper teachers are attending more math and science workshops to improve their teaching skills in these areas.

Staff Support: To replicate the project one needs to visit the school to better understand the physical facility and related activities. One day of training with follow-up sessions is helpful.

(Year initiated: 1986)

NCISE Standards met:

☑ Accessible to all students.

☑ Build on students' prior experience and knowledge.

☑ Use an instructional model based on the scientific process such as: question, discover, create, communicate, and pursue new questions.

☑ Relate to personal and social needs.

☑ Select science concepts that are developmentally appropriate, with illustrative examples drawn from the content of multiple disciplines of science.

☑ Develop scientific thinking skills such as drawing conclusions based on evidence, using inference, creating models.

☑ Develop scientific habits of mind such as curiosity, skepticism, honesty, living with ambiguity.

☑ Use authentic assessments to chart teaching and learning.

☑ Shift the role of teacher from imparter of knowledge to designer and facilitator of learning.

☑ Seek relevant and significant applications of science content and concepts to students' personal and community life.

NCTM standards met:

☐ Pose tasks based on sound and significant mathematics.

☑ Build on students' prior experience and knowledge.

☑ Develop mathematics thinking skills that convince students of the validity of particular representations, solutions, conjectures, and answers.

☑ Engage students' intellect; pose questions and tasks that elicit, engage, and challenge each students' thinking.

☑ Develop students' mathematical knowledge and skills.

☐ Stimulate students to make connections and develop a coherent framework for mathematical ideas.

☐ Call for problem formulation, problem solving, and mathematical reasoning.

☐ Promote the development of all students' dispositions to do mathematics.

☐ Develop an instructional model based on the range of ways students learn mathematics.

RESOURCES/MATERIALS NEEDED FOR ADOPTION:

The model of the space shuttle is necessary. Most of the other activities or materials could be developed locally, although gathering all available materials related to space externally (e.g., from NASA) is a better place to start.

Equipment Needed:

- VCR
- Computer Equipment - optional
- Modem
- Apple Computer
- Macintosh Computer
- Videodisc Player
- Model Space Shuttle (can be constructed by volunteers with a minimum investment for materials)

Support Needed:

- Orientation
- Staff Development
- Technical Assistance
- Workshop/Inservice

Note: See Staff Support in General Description.

FUNDED BY: N/A

CONTACT:
Mrs. Marge Masino
Science Chairperson
Sandpiper Elementary School
6724 East Hearn Road
Scottsdale, AZ 85254
(Mail Inquiries Only)

SITE(S):
Sandpiper Elementary School
6724 East Hearn Road
Scottsdale, AZ 85254

Source: Far West Laboratory

SEARCH, SOLVE, CREATE AND SHARE (SSCS)

The University of Iowa
Iowa City, IA

An Interdisciplinary Approach to Problem Solving In Math and Science

TOPIC: Multidisciplinary Studies, Elementary Math, General Math, Elementary Science, Environmental Studies Biology/Life Science, Physics, Earth/Space Science, Chemistry

USER(S): K-12 Educators, Curriculum Specialists, School Administrators, College Faculty

TARGET POPULATION: All Students

EMPHASIS ON:

Instructional Materials

- Program Packet
- Supplemental
- Learning/Teaching Materials
- Inservice Handbooks

Teaching Strategies

- Hands-On Learning
- Student-Centered Learning
- Thematic Teaching Approach
- Whole Language Approach
- Cooperative/Group Learning
- Individualized/Self-Paced Learning
- Technology-Based Strategies

Assessment Tools

- Student Assessment Materials
- Attitude Surveys/Inventories
- Teacher Reaction Inventories
- Portfolios
- Interaction Analysis - Coding Videotapes

GENERAL DESCRIPTION

Search, Solve, Create and Share is a problem-solving instructional model which provides students with concrete experiences for learning meaningful science. The student is encouraged to conduct a search of what is known and to extend that knowledge base through application or problem solving.

Innovative Features: A problem-solving instructional strategy focusing on student-centered learning, with emphasis placed on application of knowledge, is coupled with a "top-down - bottom up" inservice component that integrates higher education research perspective, K-12 administrators' leadership skills, and K-12 practitioners' knowledge of teaching-learning processes. Central to inservice is the concept of peer tutoring among teachers.

Goals: The primary goal is to provide an environment which encourages students to learn problem solving and science concepts through concrete experiences. In addition, the students expand and apply existing knowledge and critical thinking skills while generating new knowledge using a constructivist approach.

Effectiveness: Significant gains have been made in student achievement and attitude toward science, and 40% sustained use of SSCS teaching by teachers following inservice.

Staff Support: The program is implemented by K-12 educators who will need staff development directed by higher education faculty and ongoing networking with other K-12 teachers.

(Year initiated: 1984)

NCISE Standards met:

☑ Accessible to all students.

☑ Build on students' prior experience and knowledge.

☑ Use an instructional model based on the scientific process such as: question, discover, create, communicate, and pursue new questions.

☑ Relate to personal and social needs.

☑ Select science concepts that are developmentally appropriate, with illustrative examples drawn from the content of multiple disciplines of science.

☑ Develop scientific thinking skills such as drawing conclusions based on evidence, using inference, creating models.

☑ Develop scientific habits of mind such as curiosity, skepticism, honesty, living with ambiguity.

☑ Use authentic assessments to chart teaching and learning.

☑ Shift the role of teacher from imparter of knowledge to designer and facilitator of learning.

☑ Seek relevant and significant applications of science content and concepts to students' personal and community life.

NCTM standards met:

☑ Pose tasks based on sound and significant mathematics.

☑ Build on students' prior experience and knowledge.

☑ Develop mathematics thinking skills that convince students of the validity of particular representations, solutions, conjectures, and answers.

☑ Engage students' intellect; pose questions and tasks that elicit, engage, and challenge each students' thinking.

☑ Develop students' mathematical knowledge and skills.

☑ Stimulate students to make connections and develop a coherent framework for mathematical ideas.

☑ Call for problem formulation, problem solving, and mathematical reasoning.

☑ Promote the development of all students' dispositions to do mathematics.

☐ Develop an instructional model based on the range of ways students learn mathematics.

RESOURCES/MATERIALS NEEDED FOR ADOPTION:

SSCS does not require extensive materials and/or curriculum resources. No special materials are required for students. Teachers receive the SSCS Implementation Handbook to use as a resource when they are trained.

Equipment Needed:

• N/A

Support Needed:

• Staff Development

• Training Packets

• Videotapes

• Workshop/Inservice

• Consultants/Trainers

• Teacher Collaboration/Support Groups

FUNDED BY: Chapter II, National Science Foundation, Eisenhower Mathematics and Science Education Program, District, State, The University of Iowa

CONTACT:
Barbara Sandall
North Central Regional Educational Laboratory
1900 Spring Rd., Suite 300
Oak Brook, IL 60521
(708) 571-4700

SITE(S):
Iowa City Community School District
Muscatine Community School District
Ft. Dodge Community School District

(*Note:* Visitations can be arranged at these and other sites through the contact listed.)

Source: North Central Regional Educational Laboratory

SNAPFINGER ACADEMY OF MATHEMATICS, SCIENCE, AND TECHNOLOGY

Decatur, GA

A Magnet School in Math, Science and Technology for Students in Grades 4-7

TOPIC: Elementary Math, Pre-Algebra, Elementary Science, Multidisciplinary

USER(S): 4-7 Educators, School Administrators, Technology Specialists

TARGET POPULATION: Suburban, Ethnic/Minority, All Students

EMPHASIS ON:

Instructional Materials	Teaching Strategies	Assessment Tools
• N/A	• Hands-On Learning	• N/A
	• Student-Centered Learning	
	• Thematic Teaching Approach	
	• Cooperative/Group Learning	
	• Technology-Based Strategies	

GENERAL DESCRIPTION

Snapfinger is a math, science, technology magnet school for grades 4-7.

Innovative Features: Use of a guided discovery approach allows students unique opportunities to develop their mathematics and science skills as well as their critical thinking skills. Teachers learn to use an interdisciplinary approach which combines math and science. Some other innovative features include the use of the Fernbank Science Center, participation in science adventures through the Science by Mail program, and the Atlanta Math project.

Goals: The Snapfinger program adheres to standards set forth by the National Council of Teachers of Mathematics and the National Center for Improving Science Education. Its goal is to build on the students' prior knowledge and experiences and develop mathematics thinking skills that convince students of the validity of particular representations, solutions, and conjectures. A major focus of the program is the applications of science content and concepts to students' personal and community lives.

Effectiveness: Over 90% of the students in the program have elected to return. The SouthEastern Regional Vision of Education recognized the mathematics and science program as a regional program of excellence. Also, since the inception of the program, the Iowa Test of Basic Skills scores of magnet students have exceeded the scores of students within the school, the country, and the state.

Staff Support: The program is implemented by middle grade teachers interested in math, science, and technology. Training in educational technology that is continually updated is necessary for effective teachers.

(Year initiated: 1990)

NCISE Standards met:

☑ Accessible to all students.

☑ Build on students' prior experience and knowledge.

☐ Use an instructional model based on the scientific process such as: question, discover, create, communicate, and pursue new questions.

☑ Relate to personal and social needs.

☑ Select science concepts that are developmentally appropriate, with illustrative examples drawn from the content of multiple disciplines of science.

☑ Develop scientific thinking skills such as drawing conclusions based on evidence, using inference, creating models.

☑ Develop scientific habits of mind such as curiosity, skepticism, honesty, living with ambiguity.

☑ Use authentic assessments to chart teaching and learning.

☑ Shift the role of teacher from imparter of knowledge to designer and facilitator of learning.

☑ Seek relevant and significant applications of science content and concepts to students' personal and community life.

NCTM standards met:

☑ Pose tasks based on sound and significant mathematics.

☑ Build on students' prior experience and knowledge.

☑ Develop mathematics thinking skills that convince students of the validity of particular representations, solutions, conjectures, and answers.

☑ Engage students' intellect; pose questions and tasks that elicit, engage, and challenge each students' thinking.

☑ Develop students' mathematical knowledge and skills.

☑ Stimulate students to make connections and develop a coherent framework for mathematical ideas.

☑ Call for problem formulation, problem solving, and mathematical reasoning.

☑ Promote the development of all students' dispositions to do mathematics.

☑ Develop an instructional model based on the range of ways students learn mathematics.

RESOURCES/MATERIALS NEEDED FOR ADOPTION:

Fernbank Science Center Resources, Science Laboratory, mathematics manipulatives, Educator, Explorer, and overhead calculators, computer laboratories and/or work stations in each classroom

Equipment Needed:

• VCR and Monitor

• Computer Equipment

• Videodisc Player

• Special Hands-On Equipment

• State-of-the-Art Science Lab

Support Needed:

• Orientation

• Staff Development

• Videotapes

• Workshop/Inservice

• Consultants/Trainers

• Teacher Collaboration/Support Groups

Note: In order to implement and maintain a quality program in the areas of mathematics, science, and technology, it is vital to train and update teachers in the use of state-of-the-art technological equipment, innovative instructional strategies, and current standards in mathematics and science.

FUNDED BY: District

CONTACT:

SERVE Consortium for Mathematics and Science Education
345 S. Magnolia Dr., Suite D-23
Tallahassee, FL 32301-2950
(904) 922-8533; (800) 854-0476
Fax: (904) 922-8068

SITE(S):

Snapfinger School
1365 Snapfinger Road
Decatur, GA 30032

Source: SouthEastern Regional Vision for Education

SCIENCE

MIDDLE GRADES – POST SECONDARY

(includes K-12)

ENVIRONMENTAL SCIENCE SEMINAR CLASSES "MONDAY GROUPS"

Fort Myers, FL

A High School Based Environmental Science Course

TOPIC: Multidisciplinary, Environmental Studies

USER(S): 11-12 Educators, Curriculum Specialists, School Administrators, Program Planners

TARGET POPULATION: At-Risk, Ethnic/Minority, High School Students

EMPHASIS ON:

Instructional Materials	Teaching Strategies	Assessment Tools
• N/A	• Hands-On Learning	• N/A
	• Student-Centered Learning	
	• Thematic Teaching Approach	
	• Whole Language Approach	
	• Cooperative/Group Learning	
	• Individualized/Self-Paced Learning	
	• Technology-Based Strategies	

GENERAL DESCRIPTION

The program is an environmental science research class for high school juniors and seniors. It improves students' knowledge and understanding of science by engaging them in "action research" and service projects in the community.

Innovative Features: Students shape the project differently each year, based on need. All students are expected to master a common set of skills and core knowledge each year. These include action research, leadership models, conflict resolution strategies, research skills, and political action skills.

Goals: The class objective is that each student positively contributes to the chosen action research project for the year. Students are expected to demonstrate mastery of a set of core skills and basic knowledge as they contribute to the effort. They are also expected to communicate what they have learned and how they feel about their own and the class' ability to solve problems.

Effectiveness: A high percentage of students who have participated chose science and environmentally related careers with great success over the past twenty-two years.

(Year initiated: 1970)

NCISE Standards met:

☑ Accessible to all students.

☑ Build on students' prior experience and knowledge.

☑ Use an instructional model based on the scientific process such as: question, discover, create, communicate, and pursue new questions.

☑ Relate to personal and social needs.

☑ Select science concepts that are developmentally appropriate, with illustrative examples drawn from the content of multiple disciplines of science.

☑ Develop scientific thinking skills such as drawing conclusions based on evidence, using inference, creating models.

☑ Develop scientific habits of mind such as curiosity, skepticism, honesty, living with ambiguity.

☑ Use authentic assessments to chart teaching and learning.

☑ Shift the role of teacher from imparter of knowledge to designer and facilitator of learning.

☑ Seek relevant and significant applications of science content and concepts to students' personal and community life.

NCTM standards met:

☐ Pose tasks based on sound and significant mathematics.

☑ Build on students' prior experience and knowledge.

☑ Develop mathematics thinking skills that convince students of the validity of particular representations, solutions, conjectures, and answers.

☑ Engage students' intellect; pose questions and tasks that elicit, engage, and challenge each students' thinking.

☑ Develop students' mathematical knowledge and skills.

☑ Stimulate students to make connections and develop a coherent framework for mathematical ideas.

☑ Call for problem formulation, problem solving, and mathematical reasoning.

☑ Promote the development of all students' dispositions to do mathematics.

☑ Develop an instructional model based on the range of ways students learn mathematics.

RESOURCES/MATERIALS NEEDED FOR ADOPTION:

Administrative and peer support, the Monday Group article from Project Wild Guide, a packet of Monday group skill activities, a workshop on "How" is helpful to teachers and administrators.

Equipment Needed:

• Markers

• Newsprint

Support Needed:

• Orientation

• Training Packets

• Workshop/Inservice

• Project Wild Publications

Note: The program has been successfully adapted by teachers having just read the attached Project Wild article. We have found a one-to five-day workshop is very helpful to others who may be just beginning.

FUNDED BY: District, Title III

CONTACT:

SERVE Consortium for Mathematics
and Science Education
345 S. Magnolia Dr., Suite D-23
Tallahassee, FL 32301-2950
(904) 922-8533; (800) 854-0476
Fax: (904) 922-8068

SITE(S):

Lee District Schools
2055 Central Avenue
Fort Myers, FL 33901

Source: SouthEastern Regional Vision for Education

HARBOR EXPLORATIONS

University of Massachusetts-Boston, Graduate College of Education
Boston, MA

Harbor Explorations and Classroom Activities Foster Environmental and Marine Education

TOPIC: Environmental Studies, Biology/Life Science, Earth/Space Science, Chemistry

USER(S): 4-12 Educators, School Administrators

TARGET POPULATION: Urban, At-Risk, Ethnic/Minority, Female

EMPHASIS ON:

Instructional Materials	Teaching Strategies	Assessment Tools
• Supplemental Learning/Teaching Materials	• Hands-On Learning	• N/A
• Teaching Lessons/Units	• Student-Centered Learning	
	• Thematic Teaching Approach	
	• Cooperative/Group Learning	
	• Technology-Based Strategies	
	• Mentoring	

GENERAL DESCRIPTION

Harbor Explorations promotes active environmental marine education through classroom and vessel-based learning experiences.

Innovative Features: Students and teachers come to the project's research vessel, the Envirolab, to perform experiments using technologically sophisticated equipment. In the classroom, Harbor Explorations staff continue to work with teachers and students to integrate the program across the curriculum as well as within the fields of chemistry, biology, and physics. Staff also set up learning opportunities between mentor teachers, student teachers, and students. Teachers are supported by a summer institute, the annual Harbor Educators Conference and several publications.

Goals: The project provides an institutional base where teachers can improve their knowledge, skills, and research abilities using the marine environment to motivate active, on-the-water student experiences that will become part of the classroom curriculum.

Effectiveness: Evaluation of the project indicates that students make scientific discoveries, develop scientific attitudes such as curiosity and skepticism, and realize the relevancy of science to their personal lives and the environment.

Staff Support: Teachers are trained aboard the research vessel Envirolab and in the laboratory during a three week summer institute. They are assisted in curriculum development and delivery through events such as the Boston Harbor/Mass Bays Educators Conference, by publications such as "Charting Our Course," and by networking with professional organizations.

(Year initiated: 1983)

NCISE Standards met:

- ☑ Accessible to all students.
- ☐ Build on students' prior experience and knowledge.
- ☑ Use an instructional model based on the scientific process such as: question, discover, create, communicate, and pursue new questions.
- ☐ Relate to personal and social needs.
- ☑ Select science concepts that are developmentally appropriate, with illustrative examples drawn from the content of multiple disciplines of science.
- ☑ Develop scientific thinking skills such as drawing conclusions based on evidence, using inference, creating models.
- ☑ Develop scientific habits of mind such as curiosity, skepticism, honesty, living with ambiguity.
- ☐ Use authentic assessments to chart teaching and learning.
- ☑ Shift the role of teacher from imparter of knowledge to designer and facilitator of learning.
- ☑ Seek relevant and significant applications of science content and concepts to students' personal and community life.

NCTM standards met:

- ☐ Pose tasks based on sound and significant mathematics.
- ☐ Build on students' prior experience and knowledge.
- ☐ Develop mathematics thinking skills that convince students of the validity of particular representations, solutions, conjectures, and answers.
- ☐ Engage students' intellect; pose questions and tasks that elicit, engage, and challenge each students' thinking.
- ☐ Develop students' mathematical knowledge and skills.
- ☐ Stimulate students to make connections and develop a coherent framework for mathematical ideas.
- ☐ Call for problem formulation, problem solving, and mathematical reasoning.
- ☐ Promote the development of all students' dispositions to do mathematics.
- ☐ Develop an instructional model based on the range of ways students learn mathematics.

RESOURCES/MATERIALS NEEDED FOR ADOPTION:

The trip aboard Envirolab is supported with a booklet that explains the trip and gives pre and post activities. Additional materials are available, which though not necessary for participation in the program, are valuable for establishing a more complete and meaningful marine science unit. Among the low cost or free materials and services that we suggest are membership to Mass Marine Educators and their publication Flotsam & Jetsom, "Charting Our Course," an 80-page activity book based on the Gulf of Maine book but adapted for local use; Boston Harbor/Mass Bays Educators Conference, a three week summer institute for teachers and the three volume set "Investigating the Marine Environment: A Sourcebook."

Equipment Needed:

- Special Hands-On Equipment
- Curriculum Materials from Teacher Institutes

Support Needed:

- Staff Development
- Workshop/Inservice
- Teacher Collaboration/Support Groups

FUNDED BY: Eisenhower Mathematics and Science Education Program, University of Massachesetts/Boston

CONTACT:
Mike Borek
Director, Harbor Explorations
University of Massachusetts-Boston
Grad. College of Education, I.L.T.
Boston, MA 02125
(Mail Inquiries Only)

SITE(S):
University of Massachusetts-Boston
100 Morrissey Blvd
Boston, MA 02125

Source: The Regional Laboratory for Educational Improvement of the Northeast and the Islands

HIGH SCHOOL STUDENTS TEACH NEAT, WOW SCIENCE

Greenwich High School
Greenwich, CT

High School Students Teach Science in Elementary Schools

TOPIC: Elementary Science, Physics, Chemistry

USER(S): K-5 Educators, 9-12 Educators, Parents, AP Science Students

TARGET POPULATION: Honors/Advanced Placement

EMPHASIS ON:

Instructional Materials	Teaching Strategies	Assessment Tools
• A Self-Contained Program/Packet	• Hands-On Learning	• N/A
• Supplemental Learning/Teaching Materials	• Student-Centered Learning	
• Teaching Lessons/Units		

GENERAL DESCRIPTION

Goals: **NEAT-WOW** involves highly motivated high school students in the teaching of elementary school science. The program objective is to provide opportunities for elementary children to explore physical science concepts in a safe, supportive, hands-on environment.

Effectiveness: NEAT-WOW science has become an institution at this high school. Some of the school's students have initiated the teaching of elementary science lessons outside of town, and two students taught four weeks of lessons in Sitka, Alaska during the summer. Others have volunteered to teach after-school programs in their neighboring communities.

One graduate started a science teaching club at an elite university, and the club is credited with having taught more than 100 science lessons in the urban school district of the university. Two students involved in NEAT-WOW have since graduated from college and have become teachers themselves.

Staff Support: Oceanography and chemistry teachers have integrated a grading system for those students who participate in NEAT-WOW science. In addition, staff members assist students in taking NEAT-WOW as an independent study.

Administrative support is provided in the form of an aide for twelve hours per week, responsible for replenishing science boxes with materials and assisting in other managerial and organizational tasks.

(Year initiated: 1982)

NCISE Standards met:

☑ Accessible to all students.

☑ Build on students' prior experience and knowledge.

☑ Use an instructional model based on the scientific process such as: question, discover, create, communicate, and pursue new questions.

☐ Relate to personal and social needs.

☑ Select science concepts that are developmentally appropriate, with illustrative examples drawn from the content of multiple disciplines of science.

☑ Develop scientific thinking skills such as drawing conclusions based on evidence, using inference, creating models.

☑ Develop scientific habits of mind such as curiosity, skepticism, honesty, living with ambiguity.

☐ Use authentic assessments to chart teaching and learning.

☑ Shift the role of teacher from imparter of knowledge to designer and facilitator of learning.

☑ Seek relevant and significant applications of science content and concepts to students' personal and community life.

NCTM standards met:

☐ Pose tasks based on sound and significant mathematics.

☐ Build on students' prior experience and knowledge.

☐ Develop mathematics thinking skills that convince students of the validity of particular representations, solutions, conjectures, and answers.

☐ Engage students' intellect; pose questions and tasks that elicit, engage, and challenge each students' thinking.

☐ Develop students' mathematical knowledge and skills.

☐ Stimulate students to make connections and develop a coherent framework for mathematical ideas.

☐ Call for problem formulation, problem solving, and mathematical reasoning.

☐ Promote the development of all students' dispositions to do mathematics.

☐ Develop an instructional model based on the range of ways students learn mathematics.

RESOURCES/MATERIALS NEEDED FOR ADOPTION:

All together 36 different, NEAT-WOW science lessons have evolved over the past ten years. Each has been revised several times. With a little additional work, these written materials could be made available to others who wish to replicate this program.

Equipment Needed:

- Science Materials
- Household and Hardware Items

Support Needed:

- Orientation
- Staff Development
- Technical Assistance
- Workshop/Inservice
- Consultant/Trainers

FUNDED BY: District

When the program grew to more than 100 hours of instruction per year, the school district provided the services of an aide for twelve hours per week.

CONTACT:
Ron Perkins
Greenwich High School
10 Hillside Road
Greenwich, CT 06830
Fax or Mail Inquiries Only
Fax: (203) 656-3441

SITE(S):
Greenwich High School
10 Hillside Road
Greenwich, CT 06830

Source: The Regional Laboratory for Educational Improvement of the Northeast and the Islands

McQuesten Brook Wetland Study

Manchester, NH

Hands-On Environmental Education Program Fosters Student Awareness and Learning

TOPIC: Environmental Studies

USER(S): 9-12 Educators

TARGET POPULATION: Urban

EMPHASIS ON:

Instructional Materials	Teaching Strategies	Assessment Tools
• A Self-Contained Program/Packet	• Hands-On Learning	• N/A
• Supplemental Learning/Teaching Materials	• Student-Centered Learning	
• Thematic Instructional Package	• Thematic Teaching Approach	
	• Cooperative/Group Learning	

GENERAL DESCRIPTION

The Freshwater Wetlands Study Unit is a hands-on environmental education program for high school students.

Innovative Features: The curriculum includes an outdoor study location, student grouping which focuses on different aspects of the study, (e.g. botany and zoology), and involvement of professionals in the field (e.g. representatives from NH Fish and Game, UNH Cooperative Extension Office) to produce a multi-authored final report, and a student-produced video.

Goals: The main goals are to increase student awareness, interest, and involvement in a contemporary environmental issue, and to develop a custom-made curriculum on wetlands.

Effectiveness: The program has had a positive effect on student-teacher relationships, and on student attitudes and actions towards environmental issues. As a result of the project's video, younger students are now aware of environmental issues surrounding McQuesten Brook Wetland. The NH Fish and Game Department asked to utilize the program as a statewide model wetland curriculum which they will publish and provide to other schools throughout New Hampshire. All program objectives, as well as NCISE science standards were met.

(Year initiated: 1992)

NCISE Standards met:

☑ Accessible to all students.

☑ Build on students' prior experience and knowledge.

☑ Use an instructional model based on the scientific process such as: question, discover, create, communicate, and pursue new questions.

☑ Relate to personal and social needs.

☑ Select science concepts that are developmentally appropriate, with illustrative examples drawn from the content of multiple disciplines of science.

☑ Develop scientific thinking skills such as drawing conclusions based on evidence, using inference, creating models.

☑ Develop scientific habits of mind such as curiosity, skepticism, honesty, living with ambiguity.

☑ Use authentic assessments to chart teaching and learning.

☑ Shift the role of teacher from imparter of knowledge to designer and facilitator of learning.

☑ Seek relevant and significant applications of science content and concepts to students' personal and community life.

NCTM standards met:

☐ Pose tasks based on sound and significant mathematics.

☐ Build on students' prior experience and knowledge.

☐ Develop mathematics thinking skills that convince students of the validity of particular representations, solutions, conjectures, and answers.

☐ Engage students' intellect; pose questions and tasks that elicit, engage, and challenge each students' thinking.

☐ Develop students' mathematical knowledge and skills.

☐ Stimulate students to make connections and develop a coherent framework for mathematical ideas.

☐ Call for problem formulation, problem solving, and mathematical reasoning.

☐ Promote the development of all students' dispositions to do mathematics.

☐ Develop an instructional model based on the range of ways students learn mathematics.

RESOURCES/MATERIALS NEEDED FOR ADOPTION:

The resources/materials needed for adoption include: the study time-line and suggested curriculum outline; selected readings from Audubon Society, current magazines, current newspapers; wetland videos from the National Wildlife Federation and local Fish & Game Dept.; variety of field guides; water quality test kits

Equipment Needed:

- VCR
- Monitor
- Computer Equipment
- Software
- Videodisc Player
- Special Hands-On Equipment
- Water Quality Test Kits (we use HACH Kits)

Support Needed:

- N/A

Note: Local professionals were a huge asset, both for their experience, and for providing students with first-hand contact with interested adults whose jobs were related to environmental issues.

FUNDED BY: District, State, (Fish and Game, State Chemistry Lab), MIT Nuclear Research Reactor Funds

CONTACT:
Ronald N. Miller
Biology Teacher
West High School
9 Notre Dame Avenue
Manchester, NH 03102
(Mail Inquiries Only)

SITE(S):
West High School
9 Notre Dame Avenue
Manchester, NH 03102

Source: The Regional Laboratory for Educational Improvement of the Northeast and the Islands

MICROCHEMISTRY

Sandalwood High School
Jacksonville, FL

High School Microscale Chemistry Techniques

TOPIC: Chemistry

USER(S): 9-12 Educators

TARGET POPULATION: Honors/Advanced Placement, High School Students

EMPHASIS ON:

Instructional Materials	Teaching Strategies	Assessment Tools
• N/A	• Hands-On Learning	• Student Assessment Materials
	• Student-Centered Learning	• Teacher Reaction Inventories
	• Laboratory-Based Learning	

GENERAL DESCRIPTION

This program consists of over 40 lab activities using small-scale chemistry techniques in secondary school labs.

Innovative Features: The program extends the small-scale chemistry techniques begun by Dr. Hubert Alyea of Princeton University. He designed desk-top equipment for use in college chemistry courses conducted in an auditorium. This high school microchemistry lab utilizes still smaller and less expensive equipment, some of which is teacher made.

Goals: Goals are to increase student safety by using smaller amounts of chemicals, to decrease the amount of waste requiring disposal by working in drops or milligram quantities, to facilitate good science methods with techniques that permit replication and repetition within a single class period, and to increase laboratory time by integrating desk-top labs into the classroom lessons.

Effectiveness: Increased performance in first and second year chemistry has occurred with the implementation of the microscale program. Performance in classroom activities, district level tests, and AP exams have been tracked.

Staff Support: Teachers have created new laboratory activities, redesigned traditional labs at microscale, and employed many of the excellent materials developed by the high school teachers at the Woodrow Wilson Chemistry Institutes.

(Year initiated: 1987)

NCISE Standards met:

☑ Accessible to all students.

☑ Build on students' prior experience and knowledge.

☑ Use an instructional model based on the scientific process such as: question, discover, create, communicate, and pursue new questions.

☐ Relate to personal and social needs.

☐ Select science concepts that are developmentally appropriate, with illustrative examples drawn from the content of multiple disciplines of science.

☐ Develop scientific thinking skills such as drawing conclusions based on evidence, using inference, creating models.

☑ Develop scientific habits of mind such as curiosity, skepticism, honesty, living with ambiguity.

☑ Use authentic assessments to chart teaching and learning.

☑ Shift the role of teacher from imparter of knowledge to designer and facilitator of learning.

☑ Seek relevant and significant applications of science content and concepts to students' personal and community life.

NCTM standards met:

☐ Pose tasks based on sound and significant mathematics.

☐ Build on students' prior experience and knowledge.

☐ Develop mathematics thinking skills that convince students of the validity of particular representations, solutions, conjectures, and answers.

☐ Engage students' intellect; pose questions and tasks that elicit, engage, and challenge each students' thinking.

☐ Develop students' mathematical knowledge and skills.

☐ Stimulate students to make connections and develop a coherent framework for mathematical ideas.

☐ Call for problem formulation, problem solving, and mathematical reasoning.

☐ Promote the development of all students' dispositions to do mathematics.

☐ Develop an instructional model based on the range of ways students learn mathematics.

RESOURCES/MATERIALS NEEDED FOR ADOPTION:

The basic equipment in our laboratories consists of spot plates, plastic microliter plates and strips, plastic transfer (Beral) pipets, mini ice-cube trays, plastic audio tape boxes, and small conductivity testers. The inexpensive pipets and equipment regarded as disposable by industry are washed and reused, not discarded. The pipets are modified for use as dropping bottles, funnels, and gas collection devices.

All students must wear goggles and appropriate lab attire. Many laboratory activities can be implemented in a fully equipped chemistry laboratory or at a student desk. Students receive lab sets consisting of several small enclosed droppers (one inch high) in a plastic cassette box or mini ice cube tray. Open beakers of chemicals are gone. Reactions are done in small spot plates with 12, 24, or 96 wells, in lieu of test tubes. Not only is microchemistry smaller, but it is faster, permitting repeated experimentation within the confines of a fifty-minute class period.

Equipment Needed:

- Plastic Dropping Pipets
- Plastic Spot or Microculture Plate

Support Needed:

- Workshop/Inservice

Note: Inservice sessions ranging from introductory one-hour expository lessons to sixty-hour workshops with hands-on practice in approximately forty labs have served to expand the program to other schools. Sharing has also occurred at professional meetings.

FUNDED BY: Chapter II, District

CONTACT:

SERVE Consortium for Mathematics
and Science Education
345 S. Magnolia Dr., Suite D-23
Tallahassee, FL 32301-2950
(904) 922-8533; (800) 854-0476
Fax: (904) 922-8068

SITE(S):

Sandalwood High School
2750 John Prom Boulevard
Jacksonville, FL 32246

Source: SouthEastern Regional Vision for Education

OPERATION PHYSICS

Lincoln Preparatory High School
San Diego, CA

Hands-On Teaching/Learning Strategies for Ethnically Diverse High School Physics Students

TOPIC: Physics

USER(S): 9-12 Educators

TARGET POPULATION: Ethnic/Minority

EMPHASIS ON:

Instructional Materials	Teaching Strategies	Assessment Tools
• Teaching Lessons/Units	• Hands-On Learning	• N/A
	• Student-Centered Learning	
	• Thematic Teaching Approach	
	• Whole Language Teacher Approach	
	• Cooperative/Group Learning	

GENERAL DESCRIPTION

Operations Physics is designed to meet the needs of non-verbal students, especially those of ethnically diverse populations.

Innovative Features: Created for students who have English as a second language and who learn science better through hands-on teaching/learning strategies.

Goals: The goal of Operation Physics is to nurture critical thinking and a general interest and confidence in science for everyone.

Effectiveness: In 1987, this inner-city high school of 850 students offered one physics class for 17 students. Operation Physics classes began in Fall 1988. There are now three Operation Physics classes, two classes of Math-Based Physics, and one class of Advanced Placement Physics, totaling 150 students. Students feel good about themselves and science in general. More students take physics courses. Operation Physics feeds other science courses as well, and the result is a greater proportion of science-oriented students.

Staff Support: Training of more than one week, with follow-up sessions, may be required.

(Year initiated: 1988)

NCISE Standards met:

☑ Accessible to all students.

☑ Build on students' prior experience and knowledge.

☑ Use an instructional model based on the scientific process such as: question, discover, create, communicate, and pursue new questions.

☑ Relate to personal and social needs.

☑ Select science concepts that are developmentally appropriate, with illustrative examples drawn from the content of multiple disciplines of science.

☑ Develop scientific thinking skills such as drawing conclusions based on evidence, using inference, creating models.

☑ Develop scientific habits of mind such as curiosity, skepticism, honesty, living with ambiguity.

☑ Use authentic assessments to chart teaching and learning.

☑ Shift the role of teacher from imparter of knowledge to designer and facilitator of learning.

☑ Seek relevant and significant applications of science content and concepts to students' personal and community life.

NCTM standards met:

☐ Pose tasks based on sound and significant mathematics.

☐ Build on students' prior experience and knowledge.

☐ Develop mathematics thinking skills that convince students of the validity of particular representations, solutions, conjectures, and answers.

☐ Engage students' intellect; pose questions and tasks that elicit, engage, and challenge each students' thinking.

☐ Develop students' mathematical knowledge and skills.

☐ Stimulate students to make connections and develop a coherent framework for mathematical ideas.

☐ Call for problem formulation, problem solving, and mathematical reasoning.

☐ Promote the development of all students' dispositions to do mathematics.

☐ Develop an instructional model based on the range of ways students learn mathematics.

RESOURCES/MATERIALS NEEDED FOR ADOPTION:

Operation Physics materials merge content and practice and are flexible to meet local needs and constraints. The following physics-related topics are organized into loose leaf binders, which are continually being updated and revised: Behavior of Light, Sound, & Heat; Matter and Its Changes; Electricity; Forces and Motion; Energy, Color and Vision; Astronomy; Measurement; Simple Machines; Magnets and Magnetism; Forces in Fluids. The hands-on activities require only inexpensive and readily available materials.

Equipment Needed:

- VCR
- Monitor
- Manipulatives
- Computer Equipment
- Macintosh Computer
- Software

Support Needed:

- Training Packets
- Workshop/Inservice
- Consultants/Trainers

Note: Training of more than one week, with follow-up sessions, may be required.

FUNDED BY: National Science Foundation, Teacher Enhancement Funds

CONTACT:
Dr. Willa Ramsay
Physics Teacher
6677 Bonnie View Drive
San Diego, CA 92119
(Mail Inquiries Only)

SITE(S):
Lincoln Preparatory High School
150 South 49th Street
San Diego, CA 92113

Source: Far West Laboratory

OVERVIEW CASE STUDY PHYSICS (OCS)

New Mexico State University
Las Cruces, NM

Physics: From Conceptual Foundation to Case Study Problem-Solving

TOPIC: Physics

USER(S): 9-12 Educators, College Faculty

TARGET POPULATION: All Students

EMPHASIS ON:

Instructional Materials	Teaching Strategies	Assessment Tools
• Supplemental Learning/Teaching Materials	• Hands-On Learning	• N/A
• Teaching Package with Lessons/Units	• Student-Centered Learning	
	• Cooperative/Group Learning	

GENERAL DESCRIPTION

Recent research in physics education reveals serious flaws in conventional instruction for students in introductory high school and college physics courses. Students gain minimal qualitative understanding and use primitive formula-centered problem-solving strategies. Disadvantaged students are at particular risk, as research indicates those scoring low on pretests will succeed only marginally, if at all in their study.

Innovative Features: **Overview Case Study (OCS) Physics** integrates data into a flexible, spiral format that helps students build a knowledge hierarchy on a foundation of qualitative understanding. The course is divided into conceptual blocks. Each block starts with an overview in which students construct conceptual models while observing simple experiments. They learn to reason qualitatively about physical processes using sketches and diagrams and analyze similar processes quantitatively using multiple-representation, problem-solving techniques.

Two types of supplementary materials have been developed to support OCS Physics instruction: (a) an OCS Study Guide supplements a conventional text, and (b) an ALPS Kit consists of a set of Active Learning Problem Sheets that are used to transform lectures into active learning experiences.

Effectiveness: Student achievement has been evaluated using scores on qualitative tests, comprehensive problem-solving final exams, course grades, the retention of knowledge eight months after leaving the course, and the general satisfaction of students with their study of physics.

The program is being used at several large universities, at many two-year colleges, and at a variety of high schools.

(Year initiated: 1987)

NCISE Standards met:

☑ Accessible to all students.

☑ Build on students' prior experience and knowledge.

☑ Use an instructional model based on the scientific process such as: question, discover, create, communicate, and pursue new questions.

☐ Relate to personal and social needs.

☑ Select science concepts that are developmentally appropriate, with illustrative examples drawn from the content of multiple disciplines of science.

☑ Develop scientific thinking skills such as drawing conclusions based on evidence, using inference, creating models.

☑ Develop scientific habits of mind such as curiosity, skepticism, honesty, living with ambiguity.

☑ Use authentic assessments to chart teaching and learning.

☑ Shift the role of teacher from imparter of knowledge to designer and facilitator of learning.

☑ Seek to find relevant and significant applications of science content and concepts to students' personal and community life.

NCTM standards met:

☑ Pose tasks based on sound and significant mathematics.

☐ Build on students' prior experience and knowledge.

☑ Develop mathematics thinking skills that convince students of the validity of particular representations, solutions, conjectures, and answers.

☑ Engage students' intellect; pose questions and tasks that elicit, engage, and challenge each students' thinking.

☑ Develop students' mathematical knowledge and skills.

☑ Stimulate students to make connections and develop a coherent framework for mathematical ideas.

☑ Call for problem formulation, problem solving, and mathematical reasoning.

☐ Promote the development of all students' dispositions to do mathematics.

☐ Develop an instructional model based on the range of ways students learn mathematics.

RESOURCES/MATERIALS NEEDED FOR ADOPTION:

"Active Learning Problem Sheets (ALPS Kits)" and one OCS Physics Study Guide, per student.

OCS Physics Instructor's Guide.

Equipment Needed:

• None

Support Needed:

• None

Note: None is required, although in-service workshops are helpful.

FUNDED BY: National Science Foundation , Fund for the Improvement of Postsecondary Education (FIPSE)

CONTACT:

Dr. Thor Stromberg
Professor of Physics
Dept. of Physics
Department 3 D, Box 30001
New Mexico State University
Las Cruces, NM 88003
(505) 646-1811

SITE(S):

Cheri Lehman
West Lafayette High School
West Lafayette, IN 47909

Dr. Gene Mosca
U.S. Naval Academy
Annapolis, MD 21403

Source: Southwest Educational Development Laboratory

PROJECTS LABS (LEARNING ABOUT BASIC SCIENCE)

Chestnut Hill College,
Philadelphia, PA

Teacher/Scientist Teams Design Activities for Classroom Use

TOPIC: Elementary Science, Environmental Studies, Biology/Life Science, Physics

USER(S): K-12 Educators

TARGET POPULATION: Urban, Ethnic/Minority, Gifted

EMPHASIS ON:

Instructional Materials	Teaching Strategies	Assessment Tools
• Supplemental Learning/Teaching Materials	• Hands-On Learning	• N/A
• Technology-Based Materials	• Student-Centered Learning	
	• Cooperative/Group Learning	
	• Technology-Based Strategies	

GENERAL DESCRIPTION

Project LABS is an academic-industrial partnership developed by the Rohm and Haas Company. It addresses the growing need for a technically literate work force by creating technology based activities for school use.

Innovative Features: Each summer, teams of Rohm & Haas scientists and science teachers from the region spend work time at a Rohm & Haas facility developing innovative science activities. The teacher participants are selected for their competence and ability as teacher leaders. Activities developed in the summer are disseminated to other teachers during a week of inservice programs. Each Project LABS teacher conducts follow-up inservice at the local and regional level. Project LABS materials are printed and distributed by the Rohm & Haas Co.

Goals: This project has two basic goals:

(1) to improve hands-on science application activities in schools, and

(2) to foster direct involvement of scientists in science education.

Effectiveness: The effectiveness of the program depends upon the competence and enthusiasm of the teacher/scientist team. Evaluation of the activities developed are collected from all teachers involved in the program. Scientist evaluation of the program is judged by their willingness to volunteer each year.

Staff Support: This depends on whether the district wants to create a similar program or just implement the activities developed by Project LABS.

(Year initiated: 1990)

NCISE Standards met:

- ☑ Accessible to all students.
- ☑ Build on students' prior experience and knowledge.
- ☑ Use an instructional model based on the scientific process such as: question, discover, create, communicate, and pursue new questions.
- ☑ Relate to personal and social needs.
- ☐ Select science concepts that are developmentally appropriate, with illustrative examples drawn from the content of multiple disciplines of science.
- ☑ Develop scientific thinking skills such as drawing conclusions based on evidence, using inference, creating models.
- ☑ Develop scientific habits of mind such as curiosity, skepticism, honesty, living with ambiguity.
- ☐ Use authentic assessments to chart teaching and learning.
- ☑ Shift the role of teacher from imparter of knowledge to designer and facilitator of learning.
- ☑ Seek relevant and significant applications of science content and concepts to students' personal and community life.

NCTM standards met:

- ☐ Pose tasks based on sound and significant mathematics.
- ☐ Build on students' prior experience and knowledge.
- ☐ Develop mathematics thinking skills that convince students of the validity of particular representations, solutions, conjectures, and answers.
- ☐ Engage students' intellect; pose questions and tasks that elicit, engage, and challenge each students' thinking.
- ☐ Develop students' mathematical knowledge and skills.
- ☐ Stimulate students to make connections and develop a coherent framework for mathematical ideas.
- ☐ Call for problem formulation, problem solving, and mathematical reasoning.
- ☐ Promote the development of all students' dispositions to do mathematics.
- ☐ Develop an instructional model based on the range of ways students learn mathematics.

RESOURCES/MATERIALS NEEDED FOR ADOPTION:

Teachers can obtain the Project LABS materials free from the Rohm and Haas Company. (If a series of small companies each hosted a single teacher in the summer, a dissemination conference could be held in connection with a Science Teachers Association meeting).

Equipment Needed:

- N/A

Support Needed:

- Staff Development
- Workshop/Inservice
- Teacher Collaboration/Support Groups

FUNDED BY: National Science Foundation

CONTACT:

Dr. Helen Burke
Program Coordinator
Chestnut Hill College
9601 Germantown Avenue
Philadelphia, PA 19118
(215) 248-7194

SITE(S):

Chestnut Hill College
9601 Germantown Avenue
Philadelphia, PA 19118
(215) 248-7194

Source: Research for Better Schools

PROJECT LIFE

Department of Biological Sciences, LA Tech University
Ruston, LA

Revitalizing Science Education by Modeling the NSF Statewide Systemic Initiative

TOPIC: Environmental Sciences, Ecology, Human Biology

USER(S): University biology, science education faculty, and middle grades science teachers

TARGET POPULATION: All Students

EMPHASIS ON:

Instructional Materials	Teaching Strategies	Assessment Tools
• N/A	• Hands-On Learning	• Student Assessment Materials
	• Student-Centered Learning	• Attitude Surveys/Inventories
	• Thematic Teaching Approach	• Teacher Reaction Inventories
	• Whole Language Approach	• Portfolios
	• Cooperative/Group Learning	• Performance Tasks
	• Individualized/Self-Paced Learning	• Journals
	• Technology-Based Strategies	• Classroom Videotaping
		• Site Coordinator Observations

GENERAL DESCRIPTION

Project LIFE revitalizes science education in 26 parishes of North Louisiana and models reforms mandated by the National Science Foundation's (NSF's) Statewide Systemic Initiative. Teacher participants develop knowledge, skills, and confidence to use an investigative approach to teaching science. Strong follow-ups include five workshops during the school year, newsletters to teachers and students, and site visits.

Innovative Features: Modeling of reform goals is presented in an intensive three-week summer course of field and laboratory activities which teachers study relationships between organisms and their environment. For the following five weeks, participants work on advanced activities for a demonstration at Project LIFE EXPO. Teachers receive four hours of graduate credit.

Goals:
1. To improve the science content knowledge of teachers, and ultimately their students, in the areas of behavior/organism biology, ecology/population biology, and environmental science;

2. To teach science by modeling the behaviors that are used in the process that is science;

3. To capture the spirit of reforms in science espoused by the National Science Foundation and LaSIP (Louisiana Systemic Initiative Program).

Effectiveness: A variety of assessment techniques are used to evaluate the project including: portfolios, journals, hands-on performance, projects, group reports, videotapes. A formative evaluation is conducted by the instructors and a site coordinator monitors implementation in participant's classrooms.

Staff Support: On-going support of the participants is provided by the site coordinator, training team, and their administration.

(Year initiated: 1992)

NCISE Standards met:

- ☑ Accessible to all students.
- ☑ Build on students' prior experience and knowledge.
- ☑ Use an instructional model based on the scientific process such as: question, discover, create, communicate, and pursue new questions.
- ☑ Relate to personal and social needs.
- ☑ Select science concepts that are developmentally appropriate, with illustrative examples drawn from the content of multiple disciplines of science.
- ☑ Develop scientific thinking skills such as drawing conclusions based on evidence, using inference, creating models.
- ☑ Develop scientific habits of mind such as curiosity, skepticism, honesty, living with ambiguity.
- ☑ Use authentic assessments to chart teaching and learning.
- ☑ Shift the role of teacher from imparter of knowledge to designer and facilitator of learning.
- ☑ Seek to find relevant and significant applications of science content and concepts to students' personal and community life.

NCTM standards met:

- ☐ Pose tasks based on sound and significant mathematics.
- ☐ Build on students' prior experience and knowledge.
- ☐ Develop mathematics thinking skills that convince students of the validity of particular representations, solutions, conjectures, and answers.
- ☐ Engage students' intellect; pose questions and tasks that elicit, engage, and challenge each students' thinking.
- ☐ Develop students' mathematical knowledge and skills.
- ☐ Stimulate students to make connections and develop a coherent framework for mathematical ideas.
- ☐ Call for problem formulation, problem solving, and mathematical reasoning.
- ☐ Promote the development of all students' dispositions to do mathematics.
- ☐ Develop an instructional model based on the range of ways students learn mathematics.

RESOURCES/MATERIALS NEEDED FOR ADOPTION:

1. Selected activities from Project WILD, Project Learning Tree, Great Experiences in Math and Science (GEMS), Outdoor Biology Instructional Strategies (OBIS), Activities Integrating Mathematics and Science (AIMS).
2. Equipment and facilities for teaching the three-week lab and field course.

Equipment Needed:

- Computer Equipment
- Software
- Manipulatives
- Special Hands-On Equipment
- Life Sciences Equipment
- Live Animals and Plants

Support Needed:

- Orientation
- Workshop/Inservice
- Site Coordinator

Note: The following support is recommended: Orientation session of 2-3 hours for superintendents and administrators to ensure support for the program; for teachers there is an orientation to model the 3-week inservice experience; a 3-week summer course, with follow-up support for 5 weeks while teachers develop individual projects; 5 academic-year workshops and follow-up visits by the site coordinator (who was an outstanding middle-grades science teacher); a site coordinator to provide the ongoing collegial support necessary to support and sustain change in the classroom.

FUNDED BY: National Science Foundation , Eisenhower Mathematics and Science Education Program, District, State (Louisiana Systemic Initiative Project)

CONTACTS:
Linda Ramsey/David Radford, Project Co-Directors
Project LIFE: Dept. of Biological Sciences
Tech Univ.
P.O. Box 3179-T.S.
Ruston, LA 71272
(318) 257-4573; Fax: (318) 257-4288

SITE(S):
Over 26 sites in Louisiana.

Source: Southwest Educational Development Laboratory

SATURDAY SCIENCE

DuPont Jr. High School
Belle, WV

Program Teams Educators and Scientists to Develop a Science Curriculum

TOPIC: Chemistry

USER(S): 8-9 Educators, Industry Scientists

TARGET POPULATION: Suburban, Honors/Advanced Placement, At-Risk, Gifted

---

EMPHASIS ON:

Instructional Materials	**Teaching Strategies**	**Assessment Tools**
• N/A	• Hands-On Learning	• N/A
	• Student-Centered Learning	
	• Cooperative/Group Learning	

GENERAL DESCRIPTION

Saturday Science is a partnership between the school and the E.I. DuPont Corporation. Annually, the science teacher and the industry chemist author, teach, and evaluate a science curriculum which is based on the needs and experience of the volunteer students and the interests of the industry. The program is delivered in a collegial atmosphere with no grades or other formal evaluation of student progress.

Innovative Features: The program is an example of how schools and industry can form a partnership to improve educational opportunity. Unlike many partnerships, this one is instructional and collaborative. The teacher and the chemist plan and teach a hands-on laboratory chemistry class to enrich the students' scientific experience.

Goals: The program has five goals: to increase science literacy within the school community; to allow students to see themselves as future scientists; to enrich students' science experience; to provide a network of science educators and industry professionals who will aid students involved in science research; and to improve the school's ninth-grade science achievement scores.

Effectiveness: Science achievement scores have risen 12% and are now above the national average. More students elect science programs at the high school level and there is increased interest in science with students successfully involved in science fairs. Saturday Science has tripled in size in its three-year history.

Staff Support: The science teacher and the industry professional need orientation, classroom space, and limited financial support from the school and the industry. The greatest need is the administrator's understanding and approval for both educator and industrial professional.

(Year initiated: 1990)

NCISE Standards met:

☑ Accessible to all students.

☑ Build on students' prior experience and knowledge.

☑ Use an instructional model based on the scientific process such as: question, discover, create, communicate, and pursue new questions.

☐ Relate to personal and social needs.

☑ Select science concepts that are developmentally appropriate, with illustrative examples drawn from the content of multiple disciplines of science.

☑ Develop scientific thinking skills such as drawing conclusions based on evidence, using inference, creating models.

☑ Develop scientific habits of mind such as curiosity, skepticism, honesty, living with ambiguity.

☐ Use authentic assessments to chart teaching and learning.

☑ Shift the role of teacher from imparter of knowledge to designer and facilitator of learning.

☑ Seek relevant and significant applications of science content and concepts to students' personal and community life.

NCTM standards met:

☐ Pose tasks based on sound and significant mathematics.

☐ Build on students' prior experience and knowledge.

☐ Develop mathematics thinking skills that convince students of the validity of particular representations, solutions, conjectures, and answers.

☐ Engage students' intellect; pose questions and tasks that elicit, engage, and challenge each students' thinking.

☐ Develop students' mathematical knowledge and skills.

☐ Stimulate students to make connections and develop a coherent framework for mathematical ideas.

☐ Call for problem formulation, problem solving, and mathematical reasoning.

☐ Promote the development of all students' dispositions to do mathematics.

☐ Develop an instructional model based on the range of ways students learn mathematics.

RESOURCES/MATERIALS NEEDED FOR ADOPTION:

The curriculum resources are the minds of the teacher and the industry scientist involved in the program. The biggest resource is the expertise of the professional scientists in the school's community. The teachers cooperate with the industry scientists to write and deliver a curriculum that utilizes their expertise.

Equipment Needed:

- Special Hands-On Laboratory Equipment

Support Needed:

- Workshop/Inservice

Note: Since Saturday Science is a program that is driven by the needs of the specific school and local industry, a workshop to assess local resources and to train teachers and scientists in "start-up" procedures would be necessary.

FUNDED BY: Grant from E.I. DuPont, Belle, WV and E.I. DuPont, Wilmington, DE.

CONTACT:
Martha W. Mullins, Teacher
Dupont Jr. High School
121 E Central Avenue
Belle, WV 25015
(Mail Inquiries Only)

SITE:
Dupont Junior High School
201 W. Main Street
Belle, WV 25015

Source: Appalachia Educational Laboratory

SCIENCE ALLIANCE

Somerville, NJ

Alliance Between Schools and Industry Enhances Current Curricula

---

TOPIC: Science

USER(S): K-12 Educators

TARGET POPULATION: All Students

EMPHASIS ON:

Instructional Materials

- Self-Contained Program/Packet
- Supplemental Learning/Teaching Materials
- Thematic Instructional Package

Teaching Strategies

- Hands-On Learning
- Thematic Teaching Approach

Assessment Tools

- Teacher Reaction Inventories

GENERAL DESCRIPTION

Science Alliance is an education/industry collaboration that meets the increasing need for a scientifically literate population and for individuals interested in pursuing science/technology careers.

Innovative Features: Working through the partnership, scientists/engineers/technicians work with K-12 teachers to develop unique science teaching modules. The module teams then train other teachers in their use.

Goals: The main goal is to tap into the classroom experience of the teacher and the subject expertise of the scientist in order to create teaching modules around existing curricula topics. These modules approach science theory from a different perspective — a personal, practical one which integrates science with other subjects and the world.

Effectiveness: Formal outcome evaluation is now being designed and effectiveness data will be collected over the next two years. Response from both the business and education communities has been overwhelmingly positive. With 20 corporations now participating, evaluations of teachers and scientists involved in module development and training have also been extremely positive.

Staff Support: This depends on whether the districts want to create their own Alliance or just implement this program's science modules.

(Year initiated: 1991)

NCISE Standards met:

☑ Accessible to all students.

☑ Build on students' prior experience and knowledge.

☑ Use an instructional model based on the scientific process such as: question, discover, create, communicate, and pursue new questions.

☑ Relate to personal and social needs.

☑ Select science concepts that are developmentally appropriate, with illustrative examples drawn from the content of multiple disciplines of science.

☑ Develop scientific thinking skills such as drawing conclusions based on evidence, using inference, creating models.

☑ Develop scientific habits of mind such as curiosity, skepticism, honesty, living with ambiguity.

☑ Use authentic assessments to chart teaching and learning.

☑ Shift the role of teacher from imparter of knowledge to designer and facilitator of learning.

☑ Seek to find relevant and significant applications of science content and concepts to students' personal and community life.

NCTM standards met:

☐ Pose tasks based on sound and significant mathematics.

☐ Build on students' prior experience and knowledge.

☐ Develop mathematics thinking skills that convince students of the validity of particular representations, solutions, conjectures, and answers.

☐ Engage students' intellect; pose questions and tasks that elicit, engage, and challenge each students' thinking.

☐ Develop students' mathematical knowledge and skills.

☐ Stimulate students to make connections and develop a coherent framework for mathematical ideas.

☐ Call for problem formulation, problem solving, and mathematical reasoning.

☐ Promote the development of all students' dispositions to do mathematics.

☐ Develop an instructional model based on the range of ways students learn mathematics.

RESOURCES/MATERIALS NEEDED FOR ADOPTION:

Materials and curriculum resources detailed in developed modules were deliberately designed for ease of implementation. Most modules developed for grades K-6 use materials available in most kitchens or grocery stores. Modules designed for 7-12 classes use materials commonly available in school laboratories. When modules were designed using more obscure supplies, the sponsoring company donated large quantities to the teachers trained in the modules.

Equipment Needed:

• N/A

Support Needed:

• Staff Development

• Technical Assistance

• Workshops/Inservice

• Consultants/Trainers

• Teacher Collaboration/Support Groups

• Provided through volunteer services from businesses and schools

FUNDED BY: National Science Foundation, Business, School Assessment Fees

CONTACT:

Mary Rubeiro, Executive Director
P.O. Box 833
64 West End Avenue
Somerville, NJ 08876
(908) 725-6032

SITE(S):

Somerset/Hunterdon Business
and Education Partnership
P.O. Box 833
64 West End Avenue
Somerville, NJ 08876

Source: Research for Better Schools

SCIENCE MENTORSHIPS

Lively Campus
Tallahassee, FL

Mentoring program in Science for Gifted Middle School Students

TOPIC: Elementary Science

USER(S): 7-8 Educators

TARGET POPULATION: Gifted

EMPHASIS ON:

Instructional Materials

- N/A

Teaching Strategies

- Hands-On Learning
- Student-Centered Learning
- Thematic Teaching Approach
- Individualized/Self-Paced Learning
- Technology-Based Strategies

Assessment Tools

- N/A

GENERAL DESCRIPTION

This is a middle school mentorship program. Seventh and eighth-grade students with a strong interest in science apply to work with a research scientist. Students become familiar with labs and develop a relationship with scientists. Students, with the assistance of a scientist, design a project that will be completed and then described to an audience at the end of the year.

Innovative Features: Students listen to a presentation by each volunteer mentor and choose the area in which they would like to work. Students and mentors meet on a regular basis for two hours each week.

Goals: Goals are to provide gifted students with an overview of career possibilities and hands-on experiences under the direction of a science professional.

Effectiveness: Students present an overview of their semester's accomplishments at an organized poster session.

(Year initiated: 1990)

NCISE Standards met:

☐ Accessible to all students.

☐ Build on students' prior experience and knowledge.

☐ Use an instructional model based on the scientific process such as: question, discover, create, communicate, and pursue new questions.

☐ Relate to personal and social needs.

☑ Select science concepts that are developmentally appropriate, with illustrative examples drawn from the content of multiple disciplines of science.

☑ Develop scientific thinking skills such as drawing conclusions based on evidence, using inference, creating models.

☑ Develop scientific habits of mind such as curiosity, skepticism, honesty, living with ambiguity.

☑ Use authentic assessments to chart teaching and learning.

☑ Shift the role of teacher from imparter of knowledge to designer and facilitator of learning.

☑ Seek to find relevant and significant applications of science content and concepts to students' personal and community life.

NCTM standards met:

☐ Pose tasks based on sound and significant mathematics.

☐ Build on students' prior experience and knowledge.

☐ Develop mathematics thinking skills that convince students of the validity of particular representations, solutions, conjectures, and answers.

☐ Engage students' intellect; pose questions and tasks that elicit, engage, and challenge each students' thinking.

☐ Develop students' mathematical knowledge and skills.

☐ Stimulate students to make connections and develop a coherent framework for mathematical ideas.

☐ Call for problem formulation, problem solving, and mathematical reasoning.

☐ Promote the development of all students' dispositions to do mathematics.

☐ Develop an instructional model based on the range of ways students learn mathematics.

RESOURCES/MATERIALS NEEDED FOR ADOPTION:

Transportation and mentorship sites

Equipment Needed:

- N/A

Support Needed:

- Orientation
- Transportation

FUNDED BY: N/A

CONTACT:

SERVE Consortium for Mathematics and Science Education
345 S. Magnolia Dr., Suite D-23
Tallahassee, FL 32301-2950
(904) 922-8533; (800) 854-0476
Fax: (904) 922-8068

SITE(S):

Lively Campus; Academic Resource Center
500 Appleyard Drive
Tallahassee, FL 32304

Source: SouthEastern Regional Vision for Education

SCIENCE TEAMS

Rutgers University, Consortium for Educational Equity
New Brunswick, NJ

Staff Development Program for Upper Elementary and Middle School Science Teachers

TOPIC: Elementary and Middle School Science, Environmental Studies

USER(S): 4-8 Educators

TARGET POPULATION: Urban, Suburban, Rural, At-Risk, Ethnic/Minority

EMPHASIS ON:

Instructional Materials

- Thematic Instructional Package
- Teaching Lessons/Units
- Curriculum Guides

Teaching Strategies

- Hands-On Learning
- Student-Centered Learning
- Thematic Teaching Approach
- Cooperative/Group Learning
- Career Connections
- Multicultural Connections

Assessment Tools

- Student Performance Assessment Materials
- Attitude Surveys/Inventories
- Teacher Reaction Inventories
- Program Review Materials
- Needs Assessment Surveys

GENERAL DESCRIPTION

Science Teams is a staff development program which shows teachers how to use cooperative learning techniques and hands-on activities to make science fun.

Innovative Features: Science Teams provides teachers with techniques and materials for use with upper elementary students, especially minorities and young women, to promote their motivation and involvement with science and in science careers.

Goals: To improve science teaching skills of teachers in order to improve science achievement for all students. Specifically, the program tries to increase the time students spend conducting experiments, using cooperative learning, and learning about science careers and societal issues.

Effectiveness: A two-year controlled study conducted by an outside evaluator shows that the program resulted in students having positive attitudes toward science. Teachers did more hands-on science in their class, included more environmental topics in their classes, and did more science career activities with students.

Staff Support: Orientation includes special sessions and materials for principals and science supervisors.

(Year initiated: 1989)

NCISE Standards met:

☑ Accessible to all students.

☑ Build on students' prior experience and knowledge.

☑ Use an instructional model based on the scientific process such as: question, discover, create, communicate, and pursue new questions.

☑ Relate to personal and social needs.

☑ Select science concepts that are developmentally appropriate, with illustrative examples drawn from the content of multiple disciplines of science.

☑ Develop scientific thinking skills such as drawing conclusions based on evidence, using inference, creating models.

☑ Develop scientific habits of mind such as curiosity, skepticism, honesty, living with ambiguity.

☑ Use authentic assessments to chart teaching and learning.

☑ Shift the role of teacher from imparter of knowledge to designer and facilitator of learning.

☑ Seek relevant and significant applications of science content and concepts to students' personal and community life.

NCTM standards met:

☐ Pose tasks based on sound and significant mathematics.

☐ Build on students' prior experience and knowledge.

☐ Develop mathematics thinking skills that convince students of the validity of particular representations, solutions, conjectures, and answers.

☐ Engage students' intellect; pose questions and tasks that elicit, engage, and challenge each students' thinking.

☐ Develop students' mathematical knowledge and skills.

☐ Stimulate students to make connections and develop a coherent framework for mathematical ideas.

☐ Call for problem formulation, problem solving, and mathematical reasoning.

☐ Promote the development of all students' dispositions to do mathematics.

☐ Develop an instructional model based on the range of ways students learn mathematics.

RESOURCES/MATERIALS NEEDED FOR ADOPTION:

The Science Teams Teacher's Manual and video are important resources to support the implementation of the program.

Equipment Needed:

- VCR and Monitor
- Teachers' Manual
- Hands-On Materials for Lessons

Support Needed:

- Orientation
- Staff Development
- Technical Assistance
- Training Packets
- Videotapes
- Workshop/Inservice
- Consultants/Trainers

Note: Orientation includes special sessions and materials for principals and science supervisors. Technical assistance includes telephone and electronic mail to support teachers as they implement this program in the classroom.

FUNDED BY: Eisenhower Mathematics and Science Education Program, Geraldine R. Dodge Foundation, Victoria Foundation.

CONTACT:

Dr. Aleta You Mastny, Project Director
Rutgers University
Consortium for Educational Equity, Bldg. 4090
Livingston Campus
New Brunswick, NJ 08903
(908) 932-2071

SITE(S):

Rutgers University
Consortium for Educational Equity, Bldg. 4090
Livingston Campus
New Brunswick, NJ 08903
(908) 932-2071

Source: Research for Better Schools

TACO (Take A Class Outdoors)

Booneville High School
Booneville, MS

A High School Science Program for Female Students

TOPIC: General Math, Geometry, Trigonometry, Environmental Studies, Biology/Life Science, Physics, Earth/Space Science, Chemistry

USER(S): 9-12 Educators

TARGET POPULATION: Females

EMPHASIS ON:

Instructional Materials	Teaching Strategies	Assessment Tools
• N/A	• Hands-On Learning	• N/A
	• Student-Centered Learning	
	• Whole Language Approach	
	• Cooperative/Group Learning	
	• Individualized/Self-Paced Learning	
	• Technology-Based Strategies	

GENERAL DESCRIPTION

Take A Class Outdoors stimulates thinking about scientific and engineering careers, develops logical reasoning and problem-solving skills, promotes positive attitudes toward science, and increases the student's interest and knowledge about scientific work.

Innovative Features: The project has served fifty young women each semester during its first year, at a two-day retreat that was at Tishomingo State Park, Dennis, Mississippi. The natural resources of the park have been utilized to enhance classroom learning. Consultants from area colleges and universities present sessions in geology, astronomy, entomology, ecology, botany, and health. Students hold snakes, study star formations, learn about plants, collect insects, use their geometry to measure the distance across a stream, study the greenhouse effect, and drink sassafras tea.

Goals: The main goal of the program is to encourage young women to take higher level science courses and consider science related careers. The project promotes positive attitudes toward science and increases interest and knowledge about scientific work.

Effectiveness: Effectiveness is determined by pre and post evaluation, journal writings on activities, teacher assessment, the level of female enrollment, and an increase in the number of library materials borrowed from the school library. Follow-up studies of students showed increased enrollment in science related fields.

(Year initiated: 1988)

NCISE Standards met:

☐ Accessible to all students.

☑ Build on students' prior experience and knowledge.

☑ Use an instructional model based on the scientific process such as: question, discover, create, communicate, and pursue new questions.

☑ Relate to personal and social needs.

☑ Select science concepts that are developmentally appropriate, with illustrative examples drawn from the content of multiple disciplines of science.

☑ Develop scientific thinking skills such as drawing conclusions based on evidence, using inference, creating models.

☑ Develop scientific habits of mind such as curiosity, skepticism, honesty, living with ambiguity.

☑ Use authentic assessments to chart teaching and learning.

☑ Shift the role of teacher from imparter of knowledge to designer and facilitator of learning.

☑ Seek relevant and significant applications of science content and concepts to students' personal and community life.

NCTM standards met:

☑ Pose tasks based on sound and significant mathematics.

☑ Build on students' prior experience and knowledge.

☑ Develop mathematics thinking skills that convince students of the validity of particular representations, solutions, conjectures, and answers.

☑ Engage students' intellect; pose questions and tasks that elicit, engage, and challenge each students' thinking.

☑ Develop students' mathematical knowledge and skills.

☑ Stimulate students to make connections and develop a coherent framework for mathematical ideas.

☑ Call for problem formulation, problem solving, and mathematical reasoning.

☑ Promote the development of all students' dispositions to do mathematics.

☐ Develop an instructional model based on the range of ways students learn mathematics.

RESOURCES/MATERIALS NEEDED FOR ADOPTION:

Travel expense depends on site of activity and duration of trip, creative presenters, staff who see the value of the program and are willing to devote extra time to its success, administrative support, and community support.

Equipment Needed:

• Advanced Technological Equipment

Support Needed:

• Technical Assistance

• Consultants/Trainers

Note: Consultants from colleges, universities, J.L. Scott Marine Education Center, Dauphin Island Sea Lab, Fort Gadsden Historical Site, and Florida Sea Grant Extension Agency were utilized with project TACO.

FUNDED BY: Chapter II

CONTACT:

SERVE Consortium for Mathematics and Science Education
345 S. Magnolia Dr., Suite D-23
Tallahassee, FL 32301-2950
(904) 922-8533; (800) 854-0476
Fax: (904) 922-8068

SITE(S):

Booneville High School
100 B George Allen Drive
Booneville, MS 38829

Source: SouthEastern Regional Vision for Education

TOOLS FOR SCIENTIFIC THINKING-FORCE MOTION-FORCE UNIT:

A MICROCOMPUTER BASED LABORATORY

Center for Science and Mathematics Teaching, Tufts University
Medford, MA

High School Program Using Microcomputers to Help Students Attain Newtonian View of Motion & Force

TOPIC: Physics

USER(S): 9-12 Educators, Curriculum Specialists, School Administrators, Program Planners, College Faculty, Education Consultant

TARGET POPULATION: All Students

EMPHASIS ON:

Instructional Materials	Teaching Strategies	Assessment Tools
• A Self-Contained Program/Packet	• Hands-On Learning	• N/A
• Thematic Instructional Pkg.	• Student-Centered Learning	
• Teaching Lessons/Units	• Cooperative/Group Learning	
• Curriculum Guides	• Technology-Based Strategies	
• Technology-Based Materials		

GENERAL DESCRIPTION

The Microcomputer-Based Laboratory Motion/Force Unit is a program that encourages and assists students to use electronic tools to generate data from the physical world and to use the data to construct their own meaning about scientific concepts.

Innovative Features: An important feature of the Motion/Force Unit is its award-winning software which makes it possible for students to carry on detailed and sophisticated analysis of data. One program innovation is that the students themselves are frequently the objects in motion, or are the source of the force that they study. Thus, students literally experience a visceral sensation of the concepts under study.

The program promotes a constructivist approach where the teacher's role moves from purveyor of knowledge to helper and facilitator — a learner among learners who suggests alternative questions and strategies of inquiry. Consequently, students construct their own scientific concepts while practicing important scientific processes and skills using electronic equipment.

Goals: The goals of of the program are to have students attain a Newtonian view of motion and force including a through comprehension of the concepts basic to distance, velocity, acceleration, and force; to improve student graphing and other science skills, particularly data analysis; and to have students practice working effectively and productively in small groups.

Effectiveness: The Motion/Force Unit has undergone rigorous evaluation and fine-tuning during its development. Thousands of high school and university students who have used the unit have made extraordinary gains in their comprehension of basic motion and force concepts as shown by their unit pre and posttest scores.

(Year initiated: 1986)

NCISE Standards met:

- ☑ Accessible to all students.
- ☑ Build on students' prior experience and knowledge.
- ☑ Use an instructional model based on the scientific process such as: question, discover, create, communicate, and pursue new questions.
- ☐ Relate to personal and social needs.
- ☐ Select science concepts that are developmentally appropriate, with illustrative examples drawn from the content of multiple disciplines of science.
- ☑ Develop scientific thinking skills such as drawing conclusions based on evidence, using inference, creating models.
- ☑ Develop scientific habits of mind such as curiosity, skepticism, honesty, living with ambiguity.
- ☑ Use authentic assessments to chart teaching and learning.
- ☑ Shift the role of teacher from imparter of knowledge to designer and facilitator of learning.
- ☐ Seek relevant and significant applications of science content and concepts to students' personal and community life.

NCTM standards met:

- ☑ Pose tasks based on sound and significant mathematics.
- ☑ Build on students' prior experience and knowledge.
- ☑ Develop mathematics thinking skills that convince students of the validity of particular representations, solutions, conjectures, and answers.
- ☑ Engage students' intellect; pose questions and tasks that elicit, engage, and challenge each students' thinking.
- ☑ Develop students' mathematical knowledge and skills.
- ☑ Stimulate students to make connections and develop a coherent framework for mathematical ideas.
- ☑ Call for problem formulation, problem solving, and mathematical reasoning.
- ☑ Promote the development of all students' dispositions to do mathematics.
- ☑ Develop an instructional model based on the range of ways students learn mathematics.

RESOURCES/MATERIALS NEEDED FOR ADOPTION:

1. One copy of the Motion and Force Unit. This contains all necessary curricular materials for students. The unit may be copied along with a detailed teachers' curriculum guide and other important information concerning the use of microcomputer-based laboratories and the pedagogical ideas that inform the curricular materials.

2. One dynamics cart per station. (PASCO Scientific's Dynamics Cart ME-9430 is recommended.)

3. One pulley per station. (PASCO Scientific Super Pulley is recommended.)

4. One 8-foot-by-12-inch ramp per station. (The smoothest surface and most rigid material possible is recommended.)

Equipment Needed:

- Computer Equipment
- IBM Compatible
- Apple Computer
- Software
- Special Hands-On Equipment
- Macintosh Computer
- Vernier Software Motion Detector
- Vernier Force Probe
- Vernier Universal Lab Interface (If using MAC or IBM)
- QUEUE, Inc. Red Box (If using Apple II)

Support Needed:

- Orientation
- Staff Development
- Workshop/Inservice

Note: Experienced secondary physics teachers could implement this unit without any other support or assistance. However, other teachers contemplating the use of the unit might benefit from inservice training.

FUNDED BY: Federal Grants.

CONTACT:
Professor Ronald K. Thornton, Director
Center for Science and Mathematics Teaching
Tufts University
Medford, MA 02155
(Mail or Fax Inquiries Only)
Fax: (617) 627-3901

SITE(S):
Shrewsbury High School
Shrewsbury, MA

Source: The Regional Laboratory for Educational Improvement of the Northeast and the Islands

TOP CHEM

East Central University
Ada, OK

Authentic Chemistry Supplemental Lab and Teacher Prep Activities

TOPIC: Chemistry

USER(S): 9-12 Educators

TARGET POPULATION: All Students

EMPHASIS ON:

Instructional Materials	Teaching Strategies	Assessment Tools
• Supplemental Learning/Teaching Materials	• Hands-On Learning	• N/A
	• Student-Centered Learning	
	• Cooperative/Group Learning	
	• Laboratory-Based Learning	

GENERAL DESCRIPTION

Summer training institutes (begun in 1982) provide two week intensive experiences modeling developmentally appropriate laboratory teaching strategies for selected 9-12 grade chemistry teachers from throughout Oklahoma. Strategies emphasized in the program include the use of the laboratory as a discovery activity to introduce a topic, cooperative learning, and the use of pooled data. Authentic science laboratory activities that use safe, inexpensive chemicals have been collected and a book of supplemental material has been developed.

Innovative Features: **Top Chem** uses a "pooled data" approach that allows students to make "in progress" assessments and corrections and to experience variations in data without losing confidence in their conclusions.

The teacher training activities are based on sound principles of learning, and the activities are safe and use inexpensive readily-obtained materials.

Goals: The Top Chem program uses safe inexpensive activities to teach chemistry to students who are in the formal operational stage of development. Its goals are to:

1. help teachers feel comfortable with hands-on activities;

2. provide simple, safe and inexpensive activities;

3. provide supplementary activities;

4. instill in teachers a healthy skepticism and positive attitude towards science that students can emulate;

5. encourage teachers to use the lab as a discovery tool rather than a verification tool.

Effectiveness: Top Chem is the publication most often requested from the Oklahoma State Department of Education's science supervisors. More than 200 schools in Oklahoma use the materials.

(Year initiated: 1982)

NCISE Standards met:

☑ Accessible to all students.

☑ Build on students' prior experience and knowledge.

☑ Use an instructional model based on the scientific process such as: question, discover, create, communicate, and pursue new questions.

☐ Relate to personal and social needs.

☑ Select science concepts that are developmentally appropriate, with illustrative examples drawn from the content of multiple disciplines of science.

☑ Develop scientific thinking skills such as drawing conclusions based on evidence, using inference, creating models.

☑ Develop scientific habits of mind such as curiosity, skepticism, honesty, living with ambiguity.

☐ Use authentic assessments to chart teaching and learning.

☑ Shift the role of teacher from imparter of knowledge to designer and facilitator of learning.

☐ Seek to find relevant and significant applications of science content and concepts to students' personal and community life.

NCTM standards met:

☐ Pose tasks based on sound and significant mathematics.

☐ Build on students' prior experience and knowledge.

☐ Develop mathematics thinking skills that convince students of the validity of particular representations, solutions, conjectures, and answers.

☐ Engage students' intellect; pose questions and tasks that elicit, engage, and challenge each students' thinking.

☐ Develop students' mathematical knowledge and skills.

☐ Stimulate students to make connections and develop a coherent framework for mathematical ideas.

☐ Call for problem formulation, problem solving, and mathematical reasoning.

☐ Promote the development of all students' dispositions to do mathematics.

☐ Develop an instructional model based on the range of ways students learn mathematics.

RESOURCES/MATERIALS NEEDED FOR ADOPTION:

Common science laboratory equipment: balance, buret, thermometer, beakers, Erlenmeyer and Volumetric flasks, metric ruler, Bunsen burner, wash bottle, test tube rack, funnel, ringstand, stirring rod, evaporating dish, brush, test tubes, pH meter, graduated cylinder.

Chemicals and other supplies such as weighing paper, matches, paper towels, detergent, etc. Since most of the chemicals and supplies are simple materials that can be purchased in a grocery or general variety store (Wal-Mart, K-Mart, et al.) the total cost of expendable supplies for a class of 24 is about $100.00 per year.

Equipment Needed:

• High School Lab Equipment

Support Needed:

• Orientation

• Workshop/Inservice

Note: The most important concern with the use of these resources is teacher understanding of developmental learning theory and appropriate student laboratory techniques. A one day general theory and orientation session has been found to be most successful if followed by a 2- or 3-week session spent working through individual lessons with teacher colleagues.

FUNDED BY: National Science Foundation , Eisenhower Mathematics and Science Education Program, State, Lloyd Noble Foundation

CONTACT:

Donald G. Stafford
Professor of Chemistry
2202 Fullview
Ada, OK 74820
(405) 332-8000 ext. 492
Fax: (405) 521-6516

SITE(S):

East Central University
Chemistry Building
Ada, OK 74820

Source: Southwest Educational Development Laboratory

TECHNOLOGY-CENTERED PRACTICES

GRADES K-12

C²PC-Computers/Calculators Pre-Calculus

North Lamar High School
Paris, TX

Promoting Student Success in Pre-Calculus through Instructional Technology

TOPIC: Calculus, Chemistry, Physics, Technology

USER(S): 9-12 Educators, Curriculum Specialists, Technology Specialists, College Faculty

TARGET POPULATION: Rural Schools

EMPHASIS ON:

Instructional Materials	Teaching Strategies	Assessment Tools
• Supplemental Learning/Teaching Materials	• Hands-On Learning	• Student Assessment Materials
• Technology-Based Materials	• Student-Centered Learning	• Attitude Surveys/Inventories
• Special Textbooks	• Cooperative/Group Learning	• Program Review Materials
	• Technology-Based Strategies	• Technology-Based Tools

GENERAL DESCRIPTION

The **C²PC** program is built around a model in which the students and teacher use hand-held graphing calculators, and an overhead projector version of a graphing calculator to become active participants in mathematics activities.

Innovative Features: Problems are posed that are relevant to the students' interests and experiences. Students develop mathematical models and construct physical models for problem situations, and use calculators to enhance learning through visual representation of the mathematics involved.

Goals: The goals of the program are to provide equal access to mathematical power for all students, to encourage students to continue mathematics and science study, and to adequately prepare students for advanced courses at the college level.

The objectives of **C²PC** are: (1) to allow students to develop concepts about graphs and functions through interactive and user-friendly technologies, (2) to stimulate student investigation of real-world problems, and (3) to provide mathematical topics and experiences that foreshadow the study of calculus.

Effectiveness: North Lamar High School pre-calculus courses have grown from one section of about 30 students in 1988 to 48 students in three sections in 1992-93. The course is now attracting minority students and nearly equal numbers of male and female students. More students are taking Advanced Placement Calculus and more graduating seniors now taking the pre-calculus course are opting for calculus courses in college.

Staff Support: Teachers attend an intensive 5-day institute. Participants gain experience in using the graphing calculators, developing appropriate instructional strategies, and gathering and analyzing relevant data using graphing calculators. Instruction is also provided on merging graphs from calculators into MS-DOS or Macintosh computer programs to create tests, worksheets, etc.

(Year initiated: 1988)

NCISE Standards met:

☑ Accessible to all students.

☐ Build on students' prior experience and knowledge.

☐ Use an instructional model based on the scientific process such as: question, discover, create, communicate, and pursue new questions.

☐ Relate to personal and social needs.

☐ Select science concepts that are developmentally appropriate, with illustrative examples drawn from the content of multiple disciplines of science.

☐ Develop scientific thinking skills such as drawing conclusions based on evidence, using inference, creating models.

☐ Develop scientific habits of mind such as curiosity, skepticism, honesty, living with ambiguity.

☐ Use authentic assessments to chart teaching and learning.

☐ Shift the role of teacher from imparter of knowledge to designer and facilitator of learning.

☑ Seek to find relevant and significant applications of science content and concepts to students' personal and community life.

NCTM standards met:

☑ Pose tasks based on sound and significant mathematics.

☑ Build on students' prior experience and knowledge.

☑ Develop mathematics thinking skills that convince students of the validity of particular representations, solutions, conjectures, and answers.

☑ Engage students' intellect; pose questions and tasks that elicit, engage, and challenge each students' thinking.

☑ Develop students' mathematical knowledge and skills.

☑ Stimulate students to make connections and develop a coherent framework for mathematical ideas.

☑ Call for problem formulation, problem solving, and mathematical reasoning.

☑ Promote the development of all students' dispositions to do mathematics.

☑ Develop an instructional model based on the range of ways students learn mathematics.

RESOURCES/MATERIALS NEEDED FOR ADOPTION:

1. Textbooks that are calculator dependent, now available through most major textbook companies (e.g., the DeMana and Waits Pre-Calculus books by Addison-Wesley).

2. Manipulative devices: Geometric shapes and solids and trigonometric devices.

3. Graphing calculators for every student (via purchase or school check-out).

4. Overhead projector (low power) with an overhead version of a graphing calculator.

5. Dry erase boards (preferred over white screens and chalkboards). Colored dry erase markers may be used to highlight items for emphasis or to overlay a graph.

Equipment Needed:

- MS DOS Compatible Computer

- Special Hands-On Equipment

- Manipulatives

- Macintosh Computer

Support Needed:

- Staff Development

- Technical Assistance

- Workshop/Inservice

- Consultants/Trainers

- Teacher Collaboration/Support Groups

Note: Teachers attend an intensive 5-day institute contracted through Ohio State University (or, in Texas, through the Texas Education Agency). Participants gain experience in using the graphing calculators, developing appropriate instructional strategies, and gathering and analyzing relevant data using graphing calculators. Instruction is also provided on merging graphs from calculators into MS-DOS or Macintosh computer programs to create tests, worksheets, etc. A resource list of former participants and instructors is provided to assist teachers in implementing the program. An additional one-day inservice is offered for persons not familiar with the use and operation of the Texas Instruments TI-81 graphing calculator.

FUNDED BY: District, National Science Foundation grant to Ohio State University, Texas Instruments, Addison-Wesley Publishing Company

CONTACT:

Dr. Tommy Eads
Math Teacher/Technology Coordinator
3201 Lewis Lane
Paris, TX 75460
(903) 737-2020
Fax: (903) 737-2008

SITE(S):

North Lamar High School
3201 Lewis Lane
Paris, TX 75460

Source: Southwest Educational Development Laboratory

CALCULATOR MATHEMATICS CURRICULUM FOR GRADES 6-8

University of Houston
Houston, TX

Instructional Strategies and Calculator Curriculum for Middle School Mathematics

TOPIC: General Math, Technology

USER(S): 6-8 Educators

TARGET POPULATION: Urban, Suburban Students

EMPHASIS ON:

Instructional Materials	Teaching Strategies	Assessment Tools
• Supplemental Learning/Teaching Materials	• N/A	• N/A
• Teaching Lessons/Units		
• Technology-Based Materials		

GENERAL DESCRIPTION

The University of Houston/Alief ISD project is the result of a collaborative effort between a large metropolitan university and a local intermediate school district to improve mathematical instruction in grades 6-8. The use of calculators is the central focus in the curriculum. Most of the activities are for small working groups or pairs of students in order to increase student involvement and communication of their mathematical findings. Teacher notes provide questions for large group summary discussions of problem-solving strategies and/or approaches.

Innovative Features: The calculator materials are designed for exploratory purposes as well as calculation. Inductive instructional approaches are incorporated whenever possible.

Goals: 1. To explore ways in which calculators could best be used for instruction and student exploration in the middle grades. 2. To create model calculator curriculum materials for grades 6-8.

Effectiveness: The Calculator Teacher Attitude Scale has been used to make systematic classroom observations to assess the quality of instruction and amount of calculator use, and to identify the kinds of activities in which students were involved when they used calculators. It has been determined that those teachers involved in the instructional model performed significantly better than those who received only workshop training.

(Year initiated: 1990)

NCISE Standards met:

☐ Accessible to all students.

☐ Build on students' prior experience and knowledge.

☐ Use an instructional model based on the scientific process such as: question, discover, create, communicate, and pursue new questions.

☐ Relate to personal and social needs.

☐ Select science concepts that are developmentally appropriate, with illustrative examples drawn from the content of multiple disciplines of science.

☐ Develop scientific thinking skills such as drawing conclusions based on evidence, using inference, creating models.

☐ Develop scientific habits of mind such as curiosity, skepticism, honesty, living with ambiguity.

☐ Use authentic assessments to chart teaching and learning.

☐ Shift the role of teacher from imparter of knowledge to designer and facilitator of learning.

☐ Seek to find relevant and significant applications of science content and concepts to students' personal and community life.

NCTM standards met:

☑ Pose tasks based on sound and significant mathematics.

☑ Build on students' prior experience and knowledge.

☑ Develop mathematics thinking skills that convince students of the validity of particular representations, solutions, conjectures, and answers.

☑ Engage students' intellect; pose questions and tasks that elicit, engage, and challenge each students' thinking.

☑ Develop students' mathematical knowledge and skills.

☑ Stimulate students to make connections and develop a coherent framework for mathematical ideas.

☑ Call for problem formulation, problem solving, and mathematical reasoning.

☐ Promote the development of all students' dispositions to do mathematics.

☐ Develop an instructional model based on the range of ways students learn mathematics.

RESOURCES/MATERIALS NEEDED FOR ADOPTION:

The necessary resources for implementing this program include fraction and scientific calculators and the curriculum materials entitled "Explorations with Calculators: A Collection of Mathematics Activities for Grades 6-8."

Equipment Needed:

- Fraction and/or Scientific Calculators

Support Needed:

- Staff Development
- Workshops/Inservice
- Consultants/Trainers
- Teacher Collaboration/Support Groups

Note: In addition to knowledge about calculator use, necessary training for implementation of this program includes 24 hours of inservice provided in eight one-half day sessions spread throughout the year. Additional assistance would be provided through the establishment of peer coaching teams.

FUNDED BY: Eisenhower Mathematics and Science Education Program

CONTACT:

Juanita Copley and Hersholt Waxman
Co-Principal Investigators
University of Houston
College of Education
Curriculum & Instruction Department
Houston, TX 77204-5872
(713) 743-4949
Fax: (713) 743-9870

SITE(S):

Alief ISD (all 6 middle schools)
P.O. Box 68
Alief, TX 77411

Source: Southwest Educational Development Laboratory

CENTER FOR IMPROVED ENGINEERING AND SCIENCE EDUCATION

Stevens Institute of Technology - CIESE
Hoboken, NJ

School-College Collaboration for Educational Improvement Through Technology

TOPIC: General Math, Pre-Algebra, Algebra I, Geometry, Algebra II, Trigonometry, Calculus

USER(S): 7-12 Educators, Technology Specialists

TARGET POPULATION: All Students

EMPHASIS ON:

Instructional Materials	Teaching Strategies	Assessment Tools
• Supplemental Learning/Teaching Materials	• Hands-On Learning	• N/A
• Teaching Lessons/Units	• Technology-Based Strategies	
• Technology-Based Materials		

GENERAL DESCRIPTION

The Center for Improved Engineering and Science Education (CIESE) works with school districts to create programs which focus on teacher-directed computer use in mathematics instruction.

Goals: To promote the use of computers to develop and provide innovative and effective curricula and instructional strategies for math teachers. To improve math, specifically in grades 7-12, by providing opportunities to enhance learning by integrating technology into the mathematics classroom.

Effectiveness: Educational Testing Service concluded that "The CIESE project successfully reached the goals set out to be accomplished." Bank Street College of Education studied the collaborative relationship between CIESE faculty and participating teachers and concluded that all types of participants valued the collaboration and considered its achievements to be significant. Studies also showed that computer-mediated instruction increased student achievement.

Staff Support: This depends on whether the districts want to create their own collaborations with a local college or technology center, or just implement CIESE models.

(Year initiated: 1988)

NCISE Standards met:

☐ Accessible to all students.

☐ Build on students' prior experience and knowledge.

☐ Use an instructional model based on the scientific process such as: question, discover, create, communicate, and pursue new questions.

☐ Relate to personal and social needs.

☐ Select science concepts that are developmentally appropriate, with illustrative examples drawn from the content of multiple disciplines of science.

☐ Develop scientific thinking skills such as drawing conclusions based on evidence, using inference, creating models.

☐ Develop scientific habits of mind such as curiosity, skepticism, honesty, living with ambiguity.

☐ Use authentic assessments to chart teaching and learning.

☐ Shift the role of teacher from imparter of knowledge to designer and facilitator of learning.

☐ Seek relevant and significant applications of science content and concepts to students' personal and community life.

NCTM standards met:

☑ Pose tasks based on sound and significant mathematics.

☐ Build on students' prior experience and knowledge.

☑ Develop mathematics thinking skills that convince students of the validity of particular representations, solutions, conjectures, and answers.

☑ Engage students' intellect; pose questions and tasks that elicit, engage, and challenge each students' thinking.

☑ Develop students' mathematical knowledge and skills.

☐ Stimulate students to make connections and develop a coherent framework for mathematical ideas.

☑ Call for problem formulation, problem solving, and mathematical reasoning.

☐ Promote the development of all students' dispositions to do mathematics.

☑ Develop an instructional model based on the range of ways students learn mathematics.

RESOURCES/MATERIALS NEEDED FOR ADOPTION:

1. Teachers need access to hardware (IBM, Apple, MAC, Tandy, etc.).

2. Teachers need access to software. The CIESE program allows teachers to preview packages before purchase.

3. Teachers and school district personnel need access to trainers, either within the school district or at a local facility, college/university.

4. Trainers need access to either a satellite downlink or a TV/VCR hook-up, either within their district or at a local facility or college/university.

Equipment Needed:

- Computer Equipment
- Software
- VCR & Monitor

Support Needed:

- Orientation
- Staff Development
- Technical Assistance
- Training Packets
- Videotapes
- Workshop/Inservice
- Consultants/Trainers
- Teacher Collaboration/Support Groups

FUNDED BY: Eisenhower Mathematics and Science Education Program

CONTACT:

Angelina Saraceno-Corbet, Consultant
Stevens Institute of Technology - CIESE
Hoboken, NJ 07030
(201) 216-5037

SITE(S):

Stevens Institute of Technology - CIESE
Hoboken, NJ 07030
(201) 216-5037

Source: Research for Better Schools

THE GEOMETRIC SUPPOSER SERIES

Sunburst/Wings for Learning, Inc.
Pleasantville, MA

Software Program Fosters Experimentation, Inductive Reasoning, and Conjecturing Among Geometry Students

TOPIC: Geometry

USER(S): 9-12 Educators

TARGET POPULATION: All Students

EMPHASIS ON:

Instructional Materials	Teaching Strategies	Assessment Tools
• A Self-Contained Program/Packet	• N/A	• N/A
• Supplemental Learning/Teaching Materials		
• Teaching Package with Lessons/Units		
• Curriculum Guides		
• Technology-Based Materials		

GENERAL DESCRIPTION

The Geometric Supposer is a series of software programs designed to introduce experimentation, inductive reasoning, and conjecturing into the learning of geometry in secondary schools.

The series consists of four programs. Three deal with a family of geometric shapes, triangles, quadrilaterals, and circles, and allow users to create on the computer screen any construction that can be carried out with a straightedge and compass. The fourth program, the preSupposer, introduces younger students to geometric shapes, constructions, and definitions.

The software also includes supporting procedures where users can measure any element in the construction. They can add, subtract, multiply, divide, or square those measurements. They can rescale and can return to previous shapes with the same or different constructions. The software allows users to repeat constructions as procedures on other shapes.

Goals: The Supposer's objective is to enable students to explore the properties of shapes and geometric elements. They can also investigate whether the properties and consequences of a given construction on a given shape are dependent on some particular property of that shape, or whether the result can be generalized.

Effectiveness: Students improve in a variety of mathematical behaviors including making conjectures, generalizing, and making arguments, as well as constructing definitions, axioms, and theorems. They also move from intuitive to formal thinking and back again. Department exams show they learn as much geometry as students in traditional classes, but develop other skills and attitudes as well.

Staff Support: Teachers must be supported with adequate time and appropriate mechanisms for study and preparation, and with appropriate curricular materials.

(Year initiated: 1992)

NCISE Standards met:

☐ Accessible to all students.

☐ Build on students' prior experience and knowledge.

☐ Use an instructional model based on the scientific process such as: question, discover, create, communicate, and pursue new questions.

☐ Relate to personal and social needs.

☐ Select science concepts that are developmentally appropriate, with illustrative examples drawn from the content of multiple disciplines of science.

☐ Develop scientific thinking skills such as drawing conclusions based on evidence, using inference, creating models.

☐ Develop scientific habits of mind such as curiosity, skepticism, honesty, living with ambiguity.

☐ Use authentic assessments to chart teaching and learning.

☐ Shift the role of teacher from imparter of knowledge to designer and facilitator of learning.

☐ Seek relevant and significant applications of science content and concepts to students' personal and community life.

NCTM standards met:

☑ Pose tasks based on sound and significant mathematics.

☑ Build on students' prior experience and knowledge.

☑ Develop mathematics thinking skills that convince students of the validity of particular representations, solutions, conjectures, and answers.

☑ Engage students' intellect; pose questions and tasks that elicit, engage, and challenge each students' thinking.

☑ Develop students' mathematical knowledge and skills.

☑ Stimulate students to make connections and develop a coherent framework for mathematical ideas.

☑ Call for problem formulation, problem solving, and mathematical reasoning.

☑ Promote the development of all students' dispositions to do mathematics.

☑ Develop an instructional model based on the range of ways students learn mathematics.

RESOURCES/MATERIALS NEEDED FOR ADOPTION:

Equipment Needed:

• Computer Equipment

Support Needed:

• Videotapes

• Workshop/Inservice

• Teacher Collaborations/Support Groups

Note: Videotapes and support groups exist.

FUNDED BY: Education Development Center

CONTACT:
Sunburst/Wings for Learning, Inc.
101 Castleton Street
Pleasantville, NY 10570
1-800-321-7511

SITE(S):
Cambridge Rindge & Latin High School
Cambridge, MA

Source: The Regional Laboratory for Educational Improvement of the Northeast and the Islands

INTEGRATING TECHNOLOGY INTO ELEMENTARY MATH & SCIENCE (INTECH)

Miami Museum of Science, Inc.
Miami, FL

Trainers Workshop in Integrating Math, Science and Technology in Elementary Schools

TOPIC: Elementary Math, Elementary Science, Technology Education

USER(S): K-6 Educators, Science/Technology Specialists

TARGET POPULATION: All Students

EMPHASIS ON:

Instructional Materials	Teaching Strategies	Assessment Tools
• Technology-Based Materials	• Hands-On Learning	• N/A
• Trainers Resource Guide	• Student-Centered Learning	
	• Cooperative/Group Learning	
	• Individualized/Self-Paced Learning	
	• Technology-Based Strategies	

GENERAL DESCRIPTION

The **InTech** program is a "train-the-trainer" model that prepares science and technology specialists to assist teachers more effectively using technology in elementary math and science instruction. The program consists of a Trainer's Resource Guide and an InTech Institute. The Resource Guide contains step-by-step instructions and teacher enhancement activities for the conduct of five teacher inservice workshops on the use of simulation software, optical technologies, probeware, and database technology in the classroom. Prospective trainers participate in a three day "InTech Institute" where the InTech workshops are modeled.

Innovative Features: The InTech model consists of five modules: Simulations, Optical Technologies, Database, Probeware, and TechnoZoo (an integrated technology activity).

Goals: Goals are to help districts provide effective inservice in the integration of technology in K-6 math and science instruction.

Effectiveness: A third party evaluation has shown that the training has had a positive impact on participants.

Staff Support: Project staff are available to provide training and follow-up services on the InTech model.

(Year initiated: 1991)

NCISE Standards met:

☑ Accessible to all students.

☑ Build on students' prior experience and knowledge.

☑ Use an instructional model based on the scientific process such as: question, discover, create, communicate, and pursue new questions.

☑ Relate to personal and social needs.

☑ Select science concepts that are developmentally appropriate, with illustrative examples drawn from the content of multiple disciplines of science.

☑ Develop scientific thinking skills such as drawing conclusions based on evidence, using inference, creating models.

☑ Develop scientific habits of mind such as curiosity, skepticism, honesty, living with ambiguity.

☑ Use authentic assessments to chart teaching and learning.

☑ Shift the role of teacher from imparter of knowledge to designer and facilitator of learning.

☑ Seek relevant and significant applications of science content and concepts to students' personal and community life.

NCTM standards met:

☐ Pose tasks based on sound and significant mathematics.

☑ Build on students' prior experience and knowledge.

☑ Develop mathematics thinking skills that convince students of the validity of particular representations, solutions, conjectures, and answers.

☑ Engage students' intellect; pose questions and tasks that elicit, engage, and challenge each students' thinking.

☑ Develop students' mathematical knowledge and skills.

☑ Stimulate students to make connections and develop a coherent framework for mathematical ideas.

☑ Call for problem formulation, problem solving, and mathematical reasoning.

☑ Promote the development of all students' dispositions to do mathematics.

☐ Develop an instructional model based on the range of ways students learn mathematics.

RESOURCES/MATERIALS NEEDED FOR ADOPTION:

Amount of equipment and software varies depending on which of the five modules will be replicated.

Equipment Needed:

• IBM Compatible or Macintosh Computers

• Software

• Videodisc Player

• CD-ROM Player

Support Needed:

• Staff Development

• Training Materials

• Workshop/Inservice

• Consultants/Trainers

FUNDED BY: State

CONTACT:

SERVE Consortium for Mathematics
and Science Education
345 S. Magnolia Dr., Suite D-23
Tallahassee, FL 32301-2950
(904) 922-8533; (800) 854-0476
Fax: (904) 922-8068

SITE(S):

Miami Museum of Science, Inc.
3280 South Miami Avenue
Miami, FL 33129

Source: SouthEastern Regional Vision for Education

TEAMS DISTANCE LEARNING

Downey, CA

Live, Interactive Mathematics and Science Distance Learning Program Providing On-Going Staff Development

TOPIC: Elementary Math, Elementary Science, Biology/Life Science

USER(S): 4-6 Educators, Curriculum Specialists, School Administrators, State Policy Makers, Parents, State/Federal Administrators

TARGET POPULATION: All Students

EMPHASIS ON:

Instructional Materials	Teaching Strategies	Assessment Tools
• Program/Packet	• Hands-On Learning	• N/A
• Supplemental	• Student-Centered Learning	
• Learning/Teaching Materials	• Thematic Teaching Approach	
• Thematic Instructional Package	• Cooperative/Group Learning	
• Teaching Lessons/Units	• Technology-Based Strategies	
• Curriculum Guides		
• Technology-Based Materials		

GENERAL DESCRIPTION

TEAMS is based on the philosophy that all students, particularly those in at-risk inner city schools, can be challenged to be successful learners of math and science through a hands-on, constructivist approach to learning.

Innovative Features: The TEAMS model provides simultaneous teacher training and student instruction, with additional staff development for teachers and parents. TEAMS instruction provides opportunities for students to share theories and strategies for problem solving.

Goals: TEAMS seeks to improve the level of science and math instruction by providing an in-class longitudinal retraining program for elementary teachers across the United States. Through TEAMS, students learn to value mathematics and science. They become confident in their own ability to become scientific thinkers and mathematical problem solvers.

Effectiveness: The positive attitude and enthusiasm for TEAMS programs shown by parents, teachers, students, and administrators has been documented through surveys, interviews, and observations. Teachers also report greater student progress and interest in mathematics and science.

Staff Support: Those considering the TEAMS approach should be committed to continuing inservice for classroom teachers, to promoting televised instruction, to encouraging hands-on interactions, and to providing simultaneous inservice and student education.

(Year initiated: 1990)

NCISE Standards met:

☑ Accessible to all students.

☑ Build on students' prior experience and knowledge.

☑ Use an instructional model based on the scientific process such as: question, discover, create, communicate, and pursue new questions.

☑ Relate to personal and social needs.

☑ Select science concepts that are developmentally appropriate, with illustrative examples drawn from the content of multiple disciplines of science.

☑ Develop scientific thinking skills such as drawing conclusions based on evidence, using inference, creating models.

☑ Develop scientific habits of mind such as curiosity, skepticism, honesty, living with ambiguity.

☑ Use authentic assessments to chart teaching and learning.

☑ Shift the role of teacher from imparter of knowledge to designer and facilitator of learning.

☑ Seek relevant and significant applications of science content and concepts to students' personal and community life.

NCTM standards met:

☑ Pose tasks based on sound and significant mathematics.

☑ Build on students' prior experience and knowledge.

☑ Develop mathematics thinking skills that convince students of the validity of particular representations, solutions, conjectures, and answers.

☑ Engage students' intellect; pose questions and tasks that elicit, engage, and challenge each students' thinking.

☑ Develop students' mathematical knowledge and skills.

☑ Stimulate students to make connections and develop a coherent framework for mathematical ideas.

☑ Call for problem formulation, problem solving, and mathematical reasoning.

☑ Promote the development of all students' dispositions to do mathematics.

☑ Develop an instructional model based on the range of ways students learn mathematics.

RESOURCES/MATERIALS NEEDED FOR ADOPTION:

In addition to teacher support material, student instructional materials, and the science and math kits, schools must have a valid Los Angeles County Office of Education's Distance Learning Services contract in order to participate in TEAMS Distance Learning. The school instructional fee is low and TEAMS programs can be received through a variety of delivery methods, such as Ku band satellite downlink, PBS broadcasts, cable television, ITFS (microwave television systems), and videotape.

Equipment Needed:

- VCR
- Monitor
- Manipulatives
- Access to Ku Band Satellite Signal, Telephone, Fax

Support Needed:

- Classroom Instructional Materials

Note: Staff development programs are telecast throughout the year.

FUNDED BY: Chapter I, Chapter II, Eisenhower Mathematics and Science Education Program, Northrop Corporation

CONTACT:
Donald S. Lake
Senior Project Director
9300 Imperial Highway
Room 250
Downey, CA 90242-2890
(310) 922-6635

SITE(S):

Boston Public Schools, Doreen Kelly, RTC Coordinator

District of Columbia Public Schools, Wendell Boyd, RTC Coordinator

Los Angeles Unified School District, Bob Wilson, RTC Coordinator

Source: Far West Laboratory

TECH (TECHNOLOGY EDUCATION CENTER AT HEMINGWAY)

Hemingway Elementary School
Hailey, ID

Hands-On Elementary Science and Technology Program

TOPIC: Elementary Math, Pre-Algebra, Geometry, Elementary Science, Environmental Studies, Technology

USER(S): K-6 Educators, Curriculum Specialists, Technology Specialists

TARGET POPULATION: Rural, Gifted, Learning Disabilities, Emotionally Handicapped Students

EMPHASIS ON:

Instructional Materials	Teaching Strategies	Assessment Tools
• N/A	• Hands-On Learning	• N/A
	• Student-Centered Learning	
	• Thematic Teaching Approach	
	• Whole Language Approach	
	• Cooperative/Group Learning	
	• Individualized/Self-Paced Learning	
	• Technology-Based Strategies	

GENERAL DESCRIPTION

The **TECH** program provides a hands-on, minds-on, multidisciplinary environment where students of all ages and abilities apply critical thinking skills, knowledge, and the tools of technology to solve practical real world problems.

Innovative Features: TECH program is an ongoing project for all students integrating science, technology, kids and the world. TECH focuses on student problem solving, creativity, and actual hands-on experiences with science and technology, thus allowing the students to drive the curriculum. The program is a cooperative effort between school administration, parents, and community members. The TECH Room budget is totally supplied by the parent auxillary, community donations, service clubs, and grants.

Goals: The purposes of the program are to teach students to become technologically literate citizens using the real tools of technology whenever possible; to provide them with an awareness and understanding of how people direct their environment through problem-solving decisions; and to assess the effects of technology on society and the environment.

Effectiveness: Students demonstrate an awareness of science and technology careers. More female students are involved in science and technology courses beyond elementary school.

Staff Support: The program is implemented by elementary science/technology teachers who need orientation, staff development, technical assistance, and teacher support groups.

(Year initiated: 1984)

NCISE Standards met:

- ☑ Accessible to all students.
- ☑ Build on students' prior experience and knowledge.
- ☑ Use an instructional model based on the scientific process such as: question, discover, create, communicate, and pursue new questions.
- ☑ Relate to personal and social needs.
- ☑ Select science concepts that are developmentally appropriate, with illustrative examples drawn from the content of multiple disciplines of science.
- ☑ Develop scientific thinking skills such as drawing conclusions based on evidence, using inference, creating models.
- ☑ Develop scientific habits of mind such as curiosity, skepticism, honesty, living with ambiguity.
- ☑ Use authentic assessments to chart teaching and learning.
- ☑ Shift the role of teacher from imparter of knowledge to designer and facilitator of learning.
- ☑ Seek relevant and significant applications of science content and concepts to students' personal and community life.

NCTM standards met:

- ☑ Pose tasks based on sound and significant mathematics.
- ☑ Build on students' prior experience and knowledge.
- ☑ Develop mathematics thinking skills that convince students of the validity of particular representations, solutions, conjectures, and answers.
- ☑ Engage students' intellect; pose questions and tasks that elicit, engage, and challenge each students' thinking.
- ☑ Develop students' mathematical knowledge and skills.
- ☑ Stimulate students to make connections and develop a coherent framework for mathematical ideas.
- ☑ Call for problem formulation, problem solving, and mathematical reasoning.
- ☑ Promote the development of all students' dispositions to do mathematics.
- ☑ Develop an instructional model based on the range of ways students learn mathematics.

RESOURCES/MATERIALS NEEDED FOR ADOPTION:

To provide students with a true, meaningful hands-on experience — in addition to the items below, lasers, and biotechnology experiment supplies are needed. Items can be donated by parents, business and industry, and borrowed from other schools. Numerous science and technology activity books, state curriculum guides, videos, CD-ROMs, laser discs, audio recordings, magazines, and satellite broadcasts are available for both staff and student use. In addition, workshops provided by the National Science Foundation, the International Technology Education Association, the Northwest Regional Educational Laboratory, state science and technology associations, NASA, etc. facilitate this type of program. Other specific resources include: NSTA Resource Directory, Elementary Technology Education Curriculum Guide (available from University of Idaho Dissemination Center); Science and Technology Aerospace Activities (NASA & ITEA); Kids and Technology (Delmar Publishers).

Equipment Needed:

- VCR and Monitor
- Manipulatives
- IBM or Macintosh Computers
- Software
- Videodisc Player
- Special Hands-On Equipment
- Video/Audio Equipment
- Darkroom Facilities
- CD-ROM Laser Disc

Support Needed:

- Orientation
- Staff Development
- Technical Assistance
- Workshop/Inservice
- Teacher Collaboration/Support Groups

Note: Anytime technology is introduced into curriculum people need to be brought together in workshops, provided with technical assistance and staff development programs to ensure support and maximum use of such programs.

FUNDED BY: National Science Foundation, Eisenhower Mathematics and Science Education Program, District, State, Business Week, MacMillian/McGraw Hill, Rotary, Papoose Club

CONTACT:
Terry Thode
TECH Room Teacher
Box 1450
Hailey, ID 83333
(208) 726-3348

SITE(S):
Hemingway Elementary School
Box 298
Ketchum, ID 83340

Source: Northwest Regional Educational Laboratory

TECHNOLOGY FOR TEENS/SMARTLAB

Sissonville Middle School
Sissonville, WV

An Integrated Middle School Program to Teach Scientific Concepts Using Computers and Robotic Toys

TOPIC: General Math, Environmental Studies, Physics, Earth/Space Science

USER(S): 6-8 Educators

TARGET POPULATION: All Students

EMPHASIS ON:

Instructional Materials	Teaching Strategies	Assessment Tools
• Supplemental	• Hands-On Learning	• N/A
• Learning/Teaching Materials	• Student-Centered Learning	
• Technology-Based Materials	• Thematic Teaching Approach	
	• Cooperative/Group Learning	
	• Individualized/Self-Paced Learning	
	• Technology-Based Strategies	

GENERAL DESCRIPTION

Technology for Teens/SmartLab is an integrated program stressing science, mathematics, computers, and reading. The thematic units are planned collaboratively by the teachers. Its primary thrust is learning scientific concepts through the cooperative investigation of real problems using technology made available to the students through robotic toys and computers. Achievement is determined by authentic assessment measures collected in student portfolios and demonstrated in exhibitions.

Innovative Features: SmartLab stresses the cooperative efforts of the students who are in heterogeneous groups. Students are able to progress as far as they can and they are expected to help each other prepare for the exhibitions which conclude each unit and which are frequently multimedia.

Goals: The major goal of the program is to encourage students to develop problem-solving, scientific, and critical thinking skills needed for the 21st century. In addition, the interrelatedness of science and the rest of the world of knowledge is a major program thrust.

Effectiveness: Teachers report an absence of typical adolescent behavior problems. They see an increase in motivation of the students. The project plans to measure any change in student attitudes toward science using pre and posttests.

Staff Support: The program requires teacher collaboration; joint planning time is essential. Staff orientation and technology workshops are necessary for implementation.

(Year initiated: 1992)

NCISE Standards met:

☑ Accessible to all students.

☑ Build on students' prior experience and knowledge.

☑ Use an instructional model based on the scientific process such as: question, discover, create, communicate, and pursue new questions.

☑ Relate to personal and social needs.

☑ Select science concepts that are developmentally appropriate, with illustrative examples drawn from the content of multiple disciplines of science.

☑ Develop scientific thinking skills such as drawing conclusions based on evidence, using inference, creating models.

☑ Develop scientific habits of mind such as curiosity, skepticism, honesty, living with ambiguity.

☑ Use authentic assessments to chart teaching and learning.

☑ Shift the role of teacher from imparter of knowledge to designer and facilitator of learning.

☐ Seek relevant and significant applications of science content and concepts to students' personal and community life.

NCTM standards met:

☑ Pose tasks based on sound and significant mathematics.

☑ Build on students' prior experience and knowledge.

☐ Develop mathematics thinking skills that convince students of the validity of particular representations, solutions, conjectures, and answers.

☑ Engage students' intellect; pose questions and tasks that elicit, engage, and challenge each students' thinking.

☐ Develop students' mathematical knowledge and skills.

☐ Stimulate students to make connections and develop a coherent framework for mathematical ideas.

☐ Call for problem formulation, problem solving, and mathematical reasoning.

☑ Promote the development of all students' dispositions to do mathematics.

☐ Develop an instructional model based on the range of ways students learn mathematics.

RESOURCES/MATERIALS NEEDED FOR ADOPTION:

A variety of technical equipment is needed in the SmartLab including computers, robotic interfaces, CD ROMS, VCRs, Camcorders, and Laser disks. Various toys featuring pneumatics and robotics are used including MacTechnic, FisherTechnic systems, Lego's Technic I & II, Capsela's Robotic Arm, and Multibotics robotic workshop.

Equipment Needed:

• Computer Equipment

• Manipulatives

• Software

• Special Hands-On Equipment

Support Needed:

• Orientation

• Workshop/Inservice

• Teacher Collaboration/Support Group

FUNDED BY: Eisenhower Mathematics and Science Education Program

CONTACT:
Daisey Holley, Science Teacher
Sissonville Middle School
8316 Old Mill Road
Sissonville, WV 25320
(304) 348-1993

SITE(S):
Sissonville Middle School
8316 Old Mill Road
Sissonville, WV 25320

(Plus 4 Other Sites)

Source: Appalachia Educational Laboratory

APPENDICES

PRACTICES BY TOPIC

Multidisciplinary Practices: K-12

PRACTICES BY TITLE

REGIONAL EDUCATIONAL LABORATORIES

Appalachia Educational Laboratory (AEL)
P.O. Box 1348
Charleston, WV 25325
304-347-0400

(Region Served: Kentucky, Tennessee, Virginia, and West Virginia)

Far West Laboratory (FWL)
730 Harrison Street
San Francisco, CA 94107
415-565-3000

(Region Served: Arizona, California, Nevada, and Utah)

Mid-Continent Regional Educational Laboratory (McREL)
2550 S. Parker Rd., Suite 500
Aurora, CO 80014
303-337-0990

(Region Served: Colorado, Kansas, Nebraska, Missouri, Wyoming, North Dakota, and South Dakota)

North Central Regional Educational Laboratory (NCREL)
1900 Spring Road, Suite 300
Oakbrook, IL 60521
708-571-4700

(Region Served: Illinois, Indiana, Iowa, Michigan, Minnesota, Ohio, and Wisconsin)

The Regional Laboratory for Educational Improvement of the Northeast and Islands
300 Brickstone Square, Suite 900
Andover, MA 01810
508-470-0098

(Region Served: Connecticut, Maine, Massachusetts, New Hampshire, New York, Rhode Island, Vermont, Puerto Rico, and the Virgin Islands)

Northwest Regional Educational Laboratory (NWREL)
101 S.W. Main Street, Suite 500
Portland, OR 97204
503-275-9594

(Region Served: Alaska, Idaho, Oregon, Montana, and Washington)

Pacific Region Educational Laboratory (PREL)
828 Fort Street Mall, Suite 500
Honolulu, HI 96813
808-533-6000

(Region Served: American Samoa, Commonwealth of the Northern Mariana Islands, Federated States of Micronesia, Guam, Hawaii, Republic of the Marshall Islands, and Republic of Palau)

Research for Better Schools (RBS)
444 N. Third Street
Philadelphia, PA 19123
215-574-9300, ext. 280

(Region Served: Delaware, Maryland, New Jersey, Pennsylvania, and the District of Columbia)

Southeastern Regional Vision for Education (SERVE)
345 S. Magnolia Drive, Suite D-23
Tallahassee, FL 32301
904-922-2300

(Region Served: Alabama, Florida, Georgia, Mississippi, North Carolina, and South Carolina)

Southwest Educational Development Laboratory (SEDL)
211 East Seventh Street
Austin, TX 78701
512-476-6861

(Region Served: Arkansas, Louisiana, New Mexico, Oklahoma, and Texas)

REGIONAL EDUCATIONAL LABORATORIES

Appalachia Educational Laboratory (AEL)
P.O. Box 1348
Charleston, WV 25325
304-347-0400

(Region Served: Kentucky, Tennessee, Virginia, and West Virginia)

Far West Laboratory (FWL)
730 Harrison Street
San Francisco, CA 94107
415-565-3000

(Region Served: Arizona, California, Nevada, and Utah)

Mid-Continent Regional Educational Laboratory (McREL)
2550 S. Parker Road, Suite 500
Aurora, CO 80014
303-337-0990

(Region Served: Colorado, Kansas, Nebraska, Missouri, Wyoming, North Dakota, and South Dakota)

North Central Regional Educational Laboratory (NCREL)
1900 Spring Road, Suite 300
Oak Brook, IL 60521
708-571-4700

(Region Served: Illinois, Indiana, Iowa, Michigan, Minnesota, Ohio, and Wisconsin)

The Regional Laboratory for Educational Improvement of the Northeast and Islands
300 Brickstone Square, Suite 900
Andover, MA 01810
508-470-0098

(Region Served: Connecticut, Maine, Massachusetts, New Hampshire, New York, Rhode Island, Vermont, Puerto Rico, and the Virgin Islands)

Northwest Regional Educational Laboratory (NWREL)
101 S.W. Main Street, Suite 500
Portland, OR 97204
503-275-9500

(Region Served: Alaska, Idaho, Oregon, Montana, and Washington)

Pacific Region Educational Laboratory (PREL)
828 Fort Street Mall, Suite 500
Honolulu, HI 96813
808-533-6000

(Region Served: American Samoa, Commonwealth of the Northern Mariana Islands, Federated States of Micronesia, Guam, Hawaii, Republic of the Marshall Islands, and Republic of Palau)

Research for Better Schools (RBS)
444 N. Third Street
Philadelphia, PA 19123
215-574-9300, ext. 280

(Region Served: Delaware, Maryland, New Jersey, Pennsylvania, and the District of Columbia)

SouthEastern Regional Vision for Education (SERVE)
University of North Carolina at Greensboro
P.O. Box 5367
Greensboro, NC 27435; or
345 S. Magnolia Drive, Suite D-23
Tallahassee, FL 32301
904-922-2300

(Region Served: Alabama, Florida, Georgia, Mississippi, North Carolina, and South Carolina)

Southwest Educational Development Laboratory (SEDL)
211 East Seventh Street
Austin, TX 78701
512-476-6861

(Region Served: Arkansas, Louisiana, New Mexico, Oklahoma, and Texas)

Regional Eisenhower Consortia and National Clearinghouse

Eisenhower Math/Science Consortium
P.O. Box 1348
Charleston, WV 25325
304-347-0400

(Region Served: Kentucky, Tennessee, Virginia, and West Virginia)

Far West Regional Consortium for Science and Mathematics
730 Harrison Street
San Francisco, CA 94107
415-241-2730

(Region Served: Arizona, California, Nevada, and Utah)

High Plains Consortium for Mathematics and Science
2550 S. Parker Road, Suite 500
Aurora, CO 80014
303-337-0990

(Region Served: Colorado, Kansas, Nebraska, Missouri, Wyoming, North Dakota, and South Dakota)

Midwest Consortium for Mathematics and Science Education
1900 Spring Road, Suite 300
Oak Brook, IL 60521
708-571-4700

(Region Served: Illinois, Indiana, Iowa, Michigan, Minnesota, Ohio, and Wisconsin)

Regional Alliance for Mathematics and Science Education Reform
300 Brickstone Square, Suite 900
Andover, MA 01810
508-470-0098; or
235 Main Street
Montpelier, VT 05602
802-223-0463

(Region Served: Connecticut, Maine, Massachusetts, New Hampshire, New York, Rhode Island, Vermont, Puerto Rico, and the Virgin Islands)

Northwest Consortium for Mathematics and Science Teaching
101 S.W. Main Street, Suite 500
Portland, OR 97204
503-275-9594

(Region Served: Alaska, Idaho, Oregon, Montana, and Washington)

Pacific Mathematics and Science Regional Consortium
828 Fort Street Mall, Suite 500
Honolulu, HI 96813
808-533-6000

(Region Served: American Samoa, Commonwealth of the Northern Mariana Islands, Federated States of Micronesia, Guam, Hawaii, Republic of the Marshall Islands, and Republic of Palau)

Mid-Atlantic Regional Consortium for Mathematics and Science Education
444 N. Third Street
Philadelphia, PA 19123
215-574-9300, ext. 280

(Region Served: Delaware, Maryland, New Jersey, Pennsylvania, and the District of Columbia)

SERVE Consortium for Mathematics and Science Education
345 S. Magnolia Drive, Suite D-23
Tallahassee, FL 32301
904-922-8533; 800-854-0476

(Region Served: Alabama, Florida, Georgia, Mississippi, North Carolina, and South Carolina)

Southwest Consortium for the Improvement of Mathematics and Science Teaching
211 E. Seventh Street
Austin, TX 78701
512-476-6861

(Region Served: Arkansas, Louisiana, New Mexico, Oklahoma, and Texas)

Eisenhower National Clearinghouse for Mathematics and Science Education
Ohio State University
1929 Kenny Road
Columbus, OH 43210
614-292-7784